DISNEP LEARNING

ENGLISH BRAIN BOOST

GRADE **2**

NELSON

This workbook belongs to:

_____

Disney LEARNING

Published by Nelson Education Ltd.

ISBN-13: 978-0-17-685497-3
ISBN-10: 0-17-685497-5

Printed and bound in Canada
1 2 3 4   21 20 19 18

For more information contact Nelson Education Ltd.,
1120 Birchmount Road, Toronto, Ontario M1K 5G4.
Or you can visit our website at nelson.com.

Contents

Track Your Learning

START

1 2 3

25 24 23 22 21 20 19

26 27 28 29 30 31 32 33

54 53 52 51 50 49

55 56 57 58 59 60

82 81 80 79 78 77 76 75

83 84 85 86 87 88 89 90

Colour a circle for every completed activity to finish the Brain Boost learning path!

4   5   6   7   8   9   10   11

18   17   16   15   14   13   12

34   35   36   37   38   39   40

48   47   46   45   44   43   42   41

61   62   63   64   65   66   67   68

74   73   72   71   70   69

91   92   93   94   **FINISH**

Out of Order

Chief Bogo likes to keep order in Zootopia!

There is no order to the letters below. Put them in alphabetical order.

C A D B   T R Q S

_ _ _ _   _ _ _ _

O N M P   J K L I

_ _ _ _   _ _ _ _

Z Y X W   G E H F

_ _ _ _   _ _ _ _

HINT To help you, write the alphabet across the bottom of the page.

Word Blocks

Judy Hopps loves everything about being a police officer! She likes law and order.

The **purple** words are out of order. Write them in the word blocks in alphabetical order.

Word Bank

officer   badge   vest   police

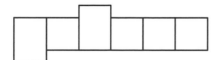

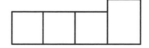

HINT Look at the shape of the word blocks and the number of letters in each word.

5

Connect the Dots

Moana must go beyond the reef to find Maui! How will she get there?

Connect the dots to find out. Follow the words in alphabetical order.

ancestor

nest   beach

Moana

canoe

lagoon   drum

kelp

jump   eel   fish

island   gull

hook

HINT When you put these words in alphabetical order, look at the first letter in each word.

Puzzle Pieces

When Te Kā is angry, she glows.
Red and yellow fire she throws!

Match the puzzle pieces to find words that rhyme. Draw a line to connect the pieces with rhyming words.

wave   sand   tree   shell

tell   free   cave   land

HINT Rhyming words sound the same. Their endings are often spelled the same way (**glows, throws**).

Solve the Rebus

Night howlers are a type of flower.
Judy Hopps learns their secret power.
Flower and **power** rhyme.

Each sentence has a secret word
that rhymes with the **purple** word.
Fill in each missing word.

Mayor Lionheart has sharp _____.

(rhymes with **paws**)

Gideon Grey bakes a delicious _____.

(rhymes with **tie**)

Nick has a bushy _____.

(rhymes with **sail**)

Judy travels to Zootopia by _____.

(rhymes with **main**)

HINT The picture gives another clue for each secret word.

Matching

Many different animals live in Zootopia. Can you name some of them?

Complete the name of each animal. Match each consonant blend with the correct word ending.

sn   unk

fr   ocodile

sk   an

cr   og

sw   ake

HINT A **consonant blend** is two or more consonants working together. You hear each letter (**gr**- in **grizzly**).

Colour to Complete

Moana has a new friend!
Who is hiding under the leaf?

Find out by colouring the shapes below. Use the Colour Key.

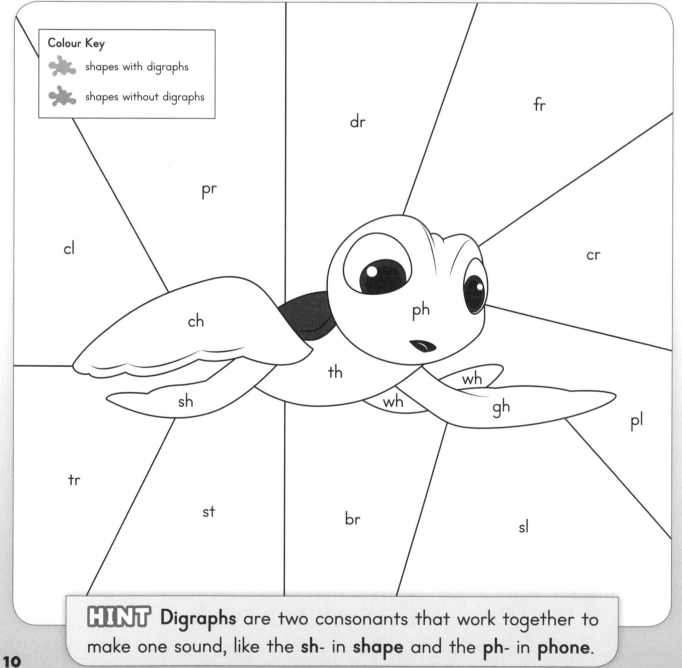

Colour Key

shapes with digraphs

shapes without digraphs

fr

dr

pr

cl

cr

ch

ph

th

wh

sh

wh

gh

pl

tr

st

br

sl

HINT Digraphs are two consonants that work together to make one sound, like the **sh-** in **shape** and the **ph-** in **phone**.

Puzzle Pieces

The heart of Te Fiti fits into Te Kā's chest like a puzzle piece!

Each consonant blend and digraph below fits with one ending. Draw a line to make a complete word.

fl

ase

ch

en

tr

eed

gr

ust

wh

ake

Fill In the Blanks

Why are so many animals in Zootopia turning savage?

To find out, fill in the missing blend or digraph in each **purple** word.

wh   pr   sh   fl   sp

1. Judy Hopps learns that night

   howlers are ____**owers**, not wolves!

2. They can make any animal go crazy, ____**edator** or prey!

3. Judy ____**eeds** back to Zootopia to find Nick Wilde.

4. They find out ____**o** is using night howlers to make animals savage.

5. It is a small ____**eep** named Bellwether!

Word Search

Mr. Big loves his family! The i in **Big** makes a short vowel sound.

In the word list, <u>underline</u> all the words with short vowel sounds. (Circle) the short vowel words in the word search.

ATE	S	R	B	J	Y	S	I	T
CAT	Z	U	P	L	Q	I	S	M
HOP	Y	N	Z	W	C	C	S	O
RUN	H	R	S	N	H	O	D	M
SIT	O	B	W	E	T	D	M	R
TOE	P	P	P	L	U	A	P	P
WET	H	G	Z	P	B	N	C	S
	E	M	R	L	C	A	T	E

HINT Short vowels sound like the vowels in **hat**, **bet**, **hit**, **hot**, and **hut**.

Word Blocks

Maui lost his hook! He cannot change shape without it.

The **a** in **change** makes a **long vowel** sound. The **a** in **shape** does, too.

<u>Underline</u> each word in the Word Bank that has a long vowel sound. Write each long vowel word in the correct box.

Word Bank

bath   log   hope   place   flap
reef   boat   use   fire   fill

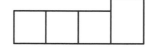   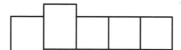

   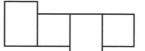

   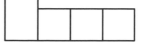

HINT Long vowels sound like their names.

Fill In the Blanks

Maui's hook helps him change into different animals.

Sometimes letters change a vowel's sound. Write the missing vowel in each word. Say the word.

 f____rk

 st____r

 c____rl

 f____r

 p____w

 c____w

 f____rst

 b____rd

HINT Look at the picture to help you figure out the word.

Fill In the Blanks

The predators of Zootopia are changing into savage beasts!

Some words change when a silent **-e** is added to the end. The short vowel becomes a long vowel.

Add a silent **-e** to each **purple** word. Write the new word on the line. Say each word.

1. You **hid** first. Now I will _____.

2. His **pal** is very _____.

3. Do **not** send a _____.

4. **Sam** has the _____ shirt.

5. **At** noon, they _____.

6. She **can** walk with a _____.

7. **Tim** is almost out of _____.

8. She wore a **cap**, not a _____.

Colour to Complete

Officer Clawhauser loves snacks! What is his favourite snack?

To find out, colour the picture. Use the Colour Key.

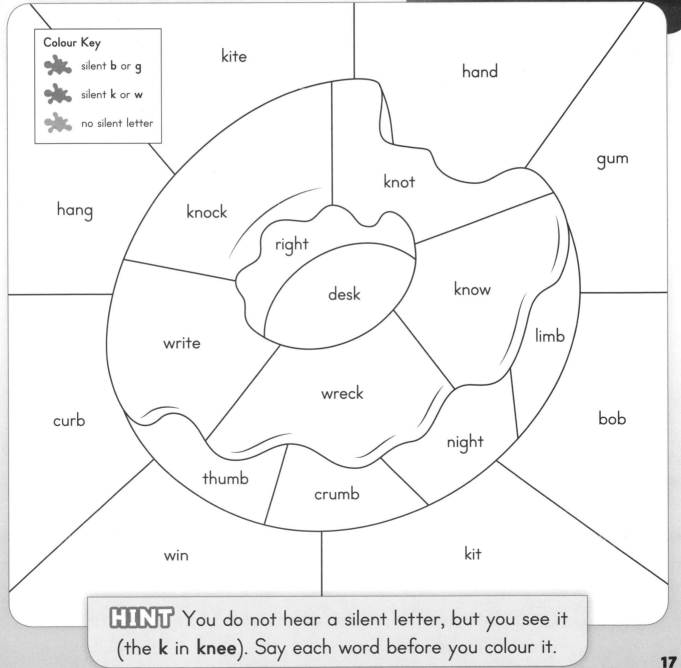

Colour Key

- silent **b** or **g**
- silent **k** or **w**
- no silent letter

kite

hand

gum

knot

hang

knock

right

desk

know

knot

limb

write

wreck

bob

curb

night

thumb

crumb

win

kit

HINT You do not hear a silent letter, but you see it (the **k** in **knee**). Say each word before you colour it.

17

Unscramble the Words

Moana turns her boat away from Te Kā. **Turn** is a verb. A **verb** is an action word.

What are some other verbs for how things move? To find out, unscramble the words.

tworh _____

snip _____

dorp _____

rlol _____

bonuce _____

trun _____

HINT All the scrambled words are verbs. Each word could complete this sentence: You can _____ the ball.

Word Search

Moana finds a hard stone in the clear water. Water is a liquid. A stone is a solid.

<u>Underline</u> words in the list that describe a solid or liquid. (Circle) those words in the word search.

BUBBLY	S Z R H G A B E R T
FOAMY	W E T P S M O O T H
GREASY	O M L U M G O L C F
ROCK	E T K H S I T B E G
ROUGH	E S R O U G H A K R
SMOOTH	Z A P R S U C Y R E
WATER	P X E S I T O F A A
WET	B U B B L Y K T D S
	K M U S D E I C M Y
	G O S V F O A M Y T

HINT Two of the words do not describe a solid or liquid. One is a type of solid. One is a type of liquid.

Maze

A savage jaguar is on the loose!
Find an escape through the maze.
Follow all the words for mammals.

Start

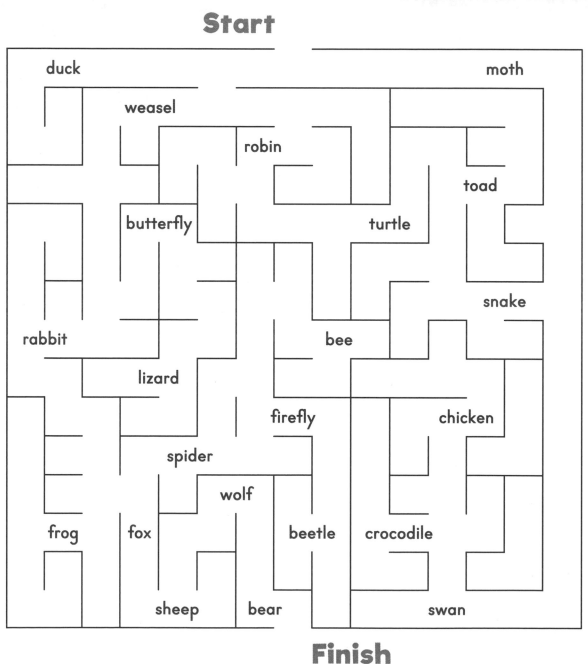

duck   moth

weasel

robin

toad

butterfly   turtle

snake

rabbit   bee

lizard

firefly   chicken

spider

wolf

frog   fox   beetle   crocodile

sheep   bear   swan

Finish

HINT A **mammal** is a warm-blooded
animal with hair or fur and a backbone.

Matching

Nick melts down frozen jumbo pops. Then he freezes the liquid into many little "pawpsicles." The pops go from solid to liquid to solid.

The pictures show water in different forms. Match each picture to the sentence that describes the water.

Ice is water that is frozen solid.

Hot water turns into a gas called steam.

Slush is a mix of liquid and frozen water.

Raindrops are liquid water.

HINT Water can take three forms: gas, liquid, or solid.

Fill In the Blanks

Moana's father is the island's chief. Someday, Moana will become the chief.

Find out how. Fill in the blanks with words from the Word Bank.

Word Bank

chief   future   sacred   stone   tradition

Chief Tui takes Moana to a mountaintop and explains

the ___ _r_ ___ ___ ___ ___ ___ ___ ___.

"This is a ___ _a_ ___ ___ ___ ___ place. A place
of chiefs. There will come a time when you will stand
on this peak and place a stone on this mountain, like
I did, like my father did, and his father, and every

___ _h_ ___ ___ ___ that has ever been. And on

that day, when you add your ___ _t_ ___ ___ ___,
you will raise this whole island higher. You are the

___ _u_ ___ ___ ___ ___ of our people, Moana."

Solve the Riddles

People in Moana's village celebrate with feasts and dancing.

People around the world celebrate many holidays. Solve each riddle with the name of a holiday.

1. I am a day to give hearts and candy to loved ones.
   I happen in February.

   What am I? _____

2. I am a day to celebrate being Canadian.
   I happen in July.

   What am I? _____

3. I am a day to wear costumes and get treats.
   I happen in October.

   What am I? _____

4. I am a day to remember people who fought for us.
   I happen in November.

   What am I? _____

Picture Search

Moana lives on an island. An island is a physical feature.

Look at each picture of a physical feature. (Circle) the word for it.

mountain   plain

stream   lake

lake   river

plain   mountain

Crossword

Moana uses stars to find her way! How else do people find their way?

Answer the clues. Solve the crossword.

Word Bank

compass   globe   scale   south

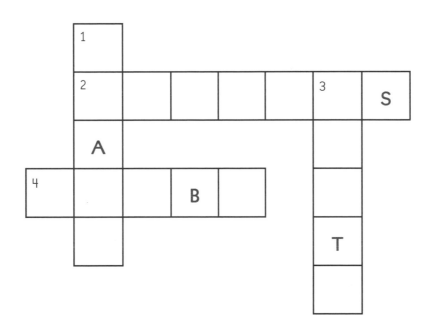

Across

2. always points to north
4. model of the earth shaped like a sphere

Down

1. use this to figure out distances on a map
3. opposite of north

Matching

Judy feels sad because she is on parking duty. Her parents feel the opposite. They are happy that she is safe.

Match each word to its opposite. Draw a line to connect them.

clean	awake
dark	quiet
asleep	dirty
large	light
loud	small

Fill In the Blanks

Judy Hopps wants a real case. How can she show Chief Bogo that she is ready?

Fill in the blanks. Write the opposite of the **purple** word that is under the line.

1. The chief thinks Judy

   is too _____.
   big

2. He believes she is _____.
   strong

3. How can she be a _____ cop?
   bad

4. She wants to prove him _____.
   right

5. She will only do her _____!
   worst

Matching

Judy Hopps belongs to a big family! Words belong to families, too.

Match each picture below to its word family. Write the picture word. Then write one other word in that family.

-elt

_____

_____

-an

_____

_____

-ox

_____

_____

HINT Say what each picture shows. Listen to the word ending.

Solve the Riddles

Officer Hopps and Nick Wilde find a clue! The word **clue** belongs to the **-ue** family.

Read the clues. Solve the word family riddles.

1. I belong to the **-ight** family. I shine.

   What am I? _____

2. I belong to the **-og** family. I once was a tree.

   What am I? _____

3. I belong to the **-ain** family. I ride on tracks.

   What am I? _____

4. I belong to the **-ank** family. I hold money.

   What am I? _____

5. I belong to the **-eck** family. I hold up your head.

   What am I? _____

Picture Search

The Kakamora attack Moana's boat! There are so many of them!

Read the list of objects. (Circle) at least two of each object in the picture. Write the plural word for each object.

sail _____   leg _____

mask _____   spear _____

hand _____   rope _____

HINT Many plural words are formed by adding an **-s**.

Unscramble the Words

Moana loves living on Motunui! What does she love about her island? To find out, unscramble each word.

Word Bank

child   fish   friend   story

fihs

_____

finerds

_____

sortsie

_____

cildhner

_____

HINT The scrambled words are plural. Check the Word Bank for the singular form of each word.

31

Fill In the Blanks

Judy Hopps must finish many tasks to become a police officer! What does Judy have to do?

To find out, fill in the missing letters to make the words plural.

Judy must leave her

parent_____, brother_____, and sister_____

to go to the police academy. Her class_____ are

difficult! She must climb wall_____ and swing

across rope course_____. The other animal_____

are bigger and stronger. But Judy works hard and

passes all the test_____. Now she can join

her hero_____ on the police force!

She can battle crook_____ and villain_____!

HINT Sometimes you need to add **-es** to make a word plural.

Word Search

Judy searches for clues about what happened to Mr. Otterton.

The word list has the singular form of each clue. Write the plural form of each word. (Circle) the plural form in the word search.

FLOWER

_____

FOX

_____

GLASS

_____

WOLF

_____

SHEEP

_____

```
S  Z  R  H  G  A  B  E  R  T
F  L  O  W  E  R  S  S  R  D  I
O  M  L  I  M  G  O  L  C  L
E  T  R  G  L  A  S  S  E  S
E  R  Y  L  E  P  X  A  T  F
Z  A  P  S  H  E  E  P  R  O
P  X  E  S  I  T  O  F  A  X
F  H  A  B  R  U  K  T  D  E
K  W  O  L  V  E  S  C  M  S
G  O  S  V  T  R  E  K  L  Q
```

Word Blocks

Te Kā hides inside a fiery exterior. Moana can see who Te Kā really is.

Can you see the base words hiding inside the **purple** words? <u>Underline</u> each base word. Fill in the word blocks with the base word.

teacher

opening

matches

fearless

melted

playful

HINT The **base word** is the main part of the word. For example, the base word of **words** is **word**.

Crack the Code

Moana finds a cave filled with huge canoes. Why are they hidden away?

To find out, fill in the blanks. Write the base word of each **purple** word. Then use the boxed letters to solve the answer.

darkness ___ ___ ___ ___

sailor ___ ___ ___ ___

monsters ___ ___ ___ ___ ___ ___

angered ___ ___ ___ ___ ___

suddenly ___ ___ ___ ___ ___

careful ___ ___ ___ ___

Moana's ancestors hid the canoes long ago when the ocean became a place of great

___ ___ ___ ___ ___ ___. They no longer wanted to sail.

HINT The number of blanks is the number of letters you need to fill in.

Crossword

Moana hears a strange knocking sound inside her canoe!

Knock is the base word of **knocking**.

Each clue has a base word. <u>Underline</u> it. Then write it in the puzzle. Solve the crossword.

Across

   2. covered

   3. endless

   4. closer

   6. humming

Down

   1. friendship

   5. loudly

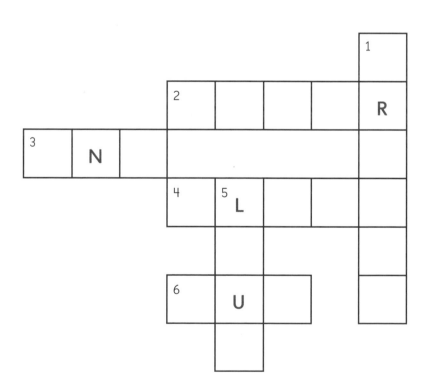

Solve the Riddles

Maui is unhappy. **Unhappy** has the prefix **un-** and the base word **happy**. Read the clues. Solve the riddles with one of the word choices. Circle the correct word to solve the riddle.

1. I mean "not tidy." What word am I?

   (un**tidy** / **pretidy**)

2. I mean "heat before." What word am I?

   (unheat / **preheat**)

3. I mean "view before." What word am I?

   (unview / **preview**)

4. I mean "not able." What word am I?

   (**unable** / preable)

5. I mean "not kind." What word am I?

   (**unkind** / prekind)

6. I mean "mix before." What word am I?

   (unmix / **premix**)

HINT The prefix **un-** means **not** and **pre-** means **before**.

Matching

Nick Wilde is dishonest when he meets Judy Hopps. She returns him to honesty.

The prefix **dis-** means "not." The prefix **re-** means "again." Match the correct prefix with the base word. Draw a line to connect them.

dis-
re-   **fresh**

dis-
re-   **able**

dis-
re-   **obey**

dis-
re-   **write**

dis-
re-   **like**

dis-
re-   **make**

HINT Say each prefix and base word together. Which combination sounds right?

Word Search

Judy Hopps and Nick Wilde uncover Bellwether's evil plan! They stop her just in time.

In the word list, <u>underline</u> all the words with prefixes. (Circle) all the words with prefixes in the word search.

DOABLE

DISARM

MISLEAD

MIXER

PREMIX

REDO

RETRY

UNDO

UNDER

```
U  Z  R  H  D  I  S  A  R  M
N  D  A  R  P  L  M  R  D  I
D  M  L  E  M  G  O  L  C  L
O  T  R  D  A  H  M  I  S  T
H  R  Y  O  D  P  X  A  T  C
Z  A  P  E  P  R  E  M  I  X
P  X  E  S  I  T  O  F  A  D
F  M  I  S  L  E  A  D  R  L
K  T  E  A  S  H  K  C  M  P
G  I  S  L  R  E  T  R  Y  T
```

HINT Prefixes include **dis-**, **mis-**, **re-**, **pre-**, and **un-**.

Fill In the Blanks

Officer Judy Hopps is short. She is shorter than Officer Nick Wilde. She is the shortest cop in Zootopia!

Adding **-er** and **-est** to words lets you compare things. Complete the sentences below. Add the right suffix to complete each word.

1. A zebra is big. A rhino is **bigg**_____.

   An elephant is the **bigg**_____ of them all.

2. A butterfly is tiny. A bee is **tini**_____.

   A fly is the **tini**_____ of them all.

3. Downtown Zootopia is hot. The rainforest

   district is **hott**_____. Sahara Square is

   the **hott**_____ of them all.

HINT A suffix attaches to the end of a word. It changes the word's meaning. The suffix **-er** means "more" and **-est** means "most."

Fill In the Blanks

The police academy is competitive! How does Judy compare to the other animals there?

To find out, fill in the missing **-er** and **-est** suffixes.

1. Judy is small_____ than the other animals at the police academy.

2. She is the small_____ animal there!

3. She may be small, but she is the tough_____.

4. She works hard_____ than anyone else.

5. She finishes with the high_____ marks in her class!

Maze

Moana and Maui must escape quickly!

Quickly has the suffix **-ly**.

Draw an escape path through the maze. Follow the words with suffixes.

Start

retake

mislead

hardly

undo

careful

harmless

slowly

Finish

unclear

redo

playful

helpful

remake

mistake

homeless

Puzzle Pieces

Moana and Maui work together against Te Kā. They have great teamwork!

Teamwork is a compound word. <u>Underline</u> the two words in **<u>team</u> <u>work</u>**.

Match the puzzle pieces. Form other compound words.

sun

water

sail

after

noon

boat

fall

set

HINT Compound words are made up of two smaller words put together.

Solve the Rebus

Moana tricks Tamatoa by replacing the heart of Te Fiti with a plain old rock!

Pictures replace the compound word in each sentence. Can you figure out what word the two pictures make? Write the compound word.

1. I went to the beach last week.

   I lost my  _____.

2. After the storm there was a

   _____. The sky was so colourful!

3. I ate my dinner so I got a treat. For dessert

   I had a   _____.

4. My favourite sport is 🧺 🏀 _____.

   I practise dribbling the ball every day.

Picture Search

The waves crash against the boat.

Some words, like **crash**, sound like what they mean. Think about what is happening in each picture. (Circle) the word that sounds like what is happening.

whoosh   slap   crunch

hum   bang   snap

smash   swish   peck

gurgle   hush   thud

Fill In the Blanks

Judy Hopps and Nick Wilde shoot out of a pipe. They plunge toward the lake.

What is happening to Judy and Nick? The action words **shoot** and **plunge** tell you.

The sentences below are missing action words. Choose the best word to complete each sentence.

1. Judy _____ (**leaps / crawls / paces**) into action when she hears a call for help.

2. Judy _____ (**walks / races / dances**) through the streets of Zootopia as fast as she can to catch the thief.

3. The jaguar _____ (**skips / sings / growls**) angrily at Judy and Nick.

4. Everyone _____ (**boos / cheers / howls**) when Nick becomes a police officer.

HINT Look for clues in the sentence to find the best word.

Matching

Judy offers to buy a juicy, fruity jumbo pop for the little elephant. How do you think the jumbo pop tastes?

Fruity and **juicy** are details about how the jumbo pop tastes. Match each detail below to a sense. Draw a line to connect them.

It is dark inside
the asylum.   smell

The wolves' eerie howls
echo in the night.   sight

The cold ice wall
stings Judy's paws.   taste

Judy takes a bite
of the sweet carrot.   sound

Judy breathes
the fresh country air.   touch

HINT Details can tell you how something
looks, tastes, feels, sounds, or smells.

47

Puzzle Pieces

Officer Hopps must pause when her paws are trapped in wet cement!

Pause and **paws** are **homophones**.

Match the puzzle pieces to find other homophone pairs. Draw a line to connect the pieces that match.

deer

knows

sale

right

sail

write

dear

nose

HINT Homophones sound the same but have different spellings and meanings. Say the words in the pieces.

Unscramble the Words

Judy Hopps and Nick Wilde hear the wolves howl. It is not safe to be here!

Besides **hear** and **here**, there are many other homophone pairs. Unscramble some homophone pairs.

 earp

_____

 airp

_____

 two

_____

 **teo**

_____

 areh

_____

 iahr

_____

 **ese**

_____

 **aes**

_____

HINT Look at the pictures to help you solve the words.

Matching

Maui says he has done many heroic things—almost too many to count!

Count the syllables in each word. Match each word to the correct number of syllables.

coconut   1 syllable

shell   2 syllables

island   3 syllables

canoe   1 syllable

warrior   2 syllables

beach   3 syllables

HINT Say each word. Clap as you say each syllable. Count the number of claps.

Crack the Code

Maui's hook is inside Tamatoa's cave! How do he and Moana get it back?

To find out, crack the code. Fill in the blanks from the Word Bank. Then use the letters in the boxes to solve the secret answer!

Word Bank

crab   digs   shiny   skeleton   treasure

▢ r ___ ___ ___ ___ ___ ___   (2 syllables)

___ ▢ ___ b ___   (1 syllable)

___ ▢ ___ g ___   (1 syllable)

___ ▢ ___ ___ ___ ___ n ___   (3 syllables)

▢ h ___ ___ ___   (2 syllables)

How do Moana and Maui escape?

Moana ___ ___ ___ ___ c ___ ___ Tamatoa!

Matching

The sloth speaks at a slow speed. The bunny is bugged beyond belief.

Read out loud each sentence above. Notice how some of the words start with the same sound. That is called **alliteration**.

Match each sentence start with its ending. The complete sentences have alliteration.

The jolly jaguar juggles   critters.

The fox finds a furry   jewels.

The creepy cage is crawling with   safety.

The silent snake slithers to   ferret.

HINT The correct ending will start with the same sound as most of the other words in the sentence.

Unscramble the Words

Judy jumps in for justice!
Unscramble each **purple** word.
Fill in the blank. Use alliteration
to complete the sentence.

Word Bank

bread   grapes   lemon   pillows   soup

1. The big bear bakes **beard** _____.

2. The little lion lost her lucky **lonem**

   _____.

3. Puppies prefer purple **pwollis** _____.

4. Silly skunks slurp **supo** _____.

5. The grumpy goat grabs **garsep** _____.

Word Search

Judy Hopps's family is happy that she graduated!

In the word list, <u>underline</u> the synonyms for **happy**. Next, complete the word search. Circle each synonym for **happy**.

BORED	B	Z	R	H	A	R	I	P	V	J
GLAD	D	P	L	E	A	S	E	D	R	O
JOLLY	P	M	L	T	M	G	O	L	C	L
JOYFUL	J	O	Y	F	U	L	M	I	S	L
MERRY	R	R	Y	O	D	L	X	A	T	Y
PLEASED	Z	T	P	E	P	R	G	L	I	K
UPSET	G	X	E	S	R	T	O	F	A	D
	L	V	D	M	R	U	A	Z	R	L
	A	T	U	O	M	E	R	R	Y	K
	D	E	S	P	Y	B	T	L	R	S

HINT Synonyms are words that have the same meaning (**small, tiny**).

Maze

Judy Hopps questions a big elephant named Nangi. What synonyms could Judy use for **big**?

To get through the maze, follow the synonyms for **big**.

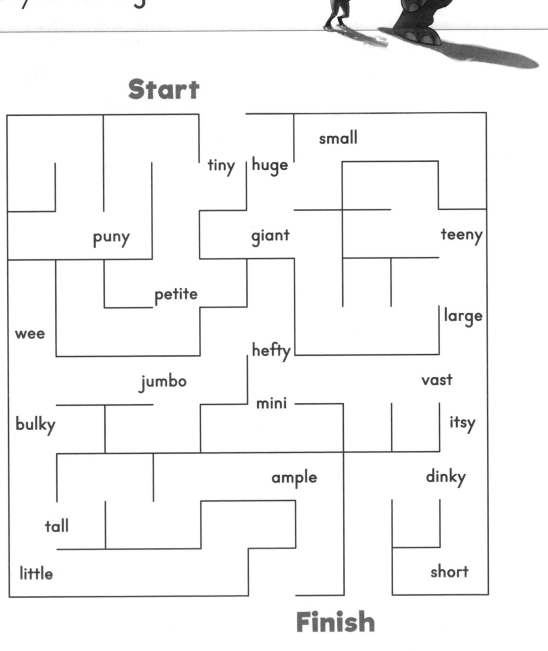

Matching

Moana rushes to find Maui. Together, they'll return the heart of Te Fiti.

Contractions help when you're in a hurry. A contraction combines two words into one shorter word.

Match each contraction to the words that form it.

I'm   you have

they're   is not

you've   they will

isn't   they are

they'll   I am

HINT **Contractions** replace one or more letters with an apostrophe. Look for the letters that are still in the contraction.

Crack the Code

Moana discovers a secret about her ancestors. What does she find out?

Combine the words to make contractions. Then use the boxed letters to solve the secret message!

I have   ___ ' ___ ___

could not   ___ ___ ___ ___ ___ ' ___

you are   ___ ___ ___ ' ___ ___

have not   ___ ___ ___ ___ ___ ' ___

might have   ___ ___ ___ ___ ___ ' ___

he will   ___ ___ ' ___ ___

Moana discovers that her ancestors were

___ ___ ___ ___ ___ ___ r ___ s !

Picture Search

Chief Tui is angry. He is frowning. It looks as if he is speaking harshly.

What do these pictures tell you about Moana, Gramma Tala, and Maui?

Circle the best answer to each question.

How does Moana feel?

angry

bored

excited

What is Gramma Tala doing?

telling a story

comforting Moana

brushing Moana's hair

What is Moana doing?

showing off her necklace

asking for help

yelling at Maui

What is Moana doing?

fixing her boat

breaking her boat

sailing her boat

Picture Search

Read the title of this story. Look at the picture. What do you think this story is about?

_____

_____

_____

_____

_____

Picture Search

Judy Hopps and Nick Wilde find out that Mayor Lionheart has all the missing predators locked up! Judy records Mayor Lionheart saying he wants to hide the animals from everyone, including the police! As soon as they can, Judy and Nick tell Chief Bogo what the mayor has been up to.

What do you think happens next? (Circle) that picture.

Explain why you chose that picture.

_____

_____

Matching

Read the story. Match each sentence below to the word **fact** or **opinion**.

Young Judy Hopps thinks being a cop is the best job. She plans to move to Zootopia and become a cop. Everyone thinks bunnies are too small to be cops.

Judy proves them wrong! She gets the highest marks at the police academy. She becomes the first bunny cop in Zootopia. Judy's parents worry about her. They think being a cop is too dangerous.

Everyone thinks Judy is too small to be a cop.   fact

Judy is the first bunny cop.   opinion

Judy's parents think being a cop is too dangerous.   fact

Judy gets the highest marks at the police academy.   opinion

HINT A **fact** is true (the sky is blue). An **opinion** is something someone thinks or feels (I think blue skies are beautiful).

Fill In the Blanks

Judy's protective parents hug her tightly. **Protective** is a detail that gives you information.

Fill in the blanks with words from the Word Bank.

Word Bank

best   first   highest   small   Young

1. _____ Judy Hopps thinks being a cop

   is the _____ job.

2. Everyone thinks bunnies are too _____ to be cops.

3. Judy gets the _____ marks at the police academy.

4. She becomes the _____ bunny cop in Zootopia.

HINT Use the text on page 62 to help you find the details.

Matching

Stories start with a **beginning**. In the middle is a **problem** and a **solution**. Then comes the **ending**. Match each section of the story to a label.

After many challenges, Moana returns Te Fiti's heart. Moana saves her island!

beginning

When Moana is sixteen she feels the pull of the ocean. She sails past the reef to find Maui and return the heart.

problem

Chief Tui does not want his people to sail past the reef. The ocean is too dangerous. Moana is not allowed to return the heart.

solution

When Moana is a baby, the ocean chooses her to return Te Fiti's heart.

ending

HINT When you finish, read the sentences in order. The story should make sense from beginning to ending.

Out of Order

Read the text. Then look at the pictures.
Number the pictures to put them in order.

Moana feels sad. She does not think she can return
Te Fiti's heart. She tosses the heart into the ocean.
She tells the ocean it made a mistake choosing her.
Suddenly, Gramma Tala appears! She shows Moana
that she can do it. Moana dives into the water to get
the heart. She believes she can finish her task.

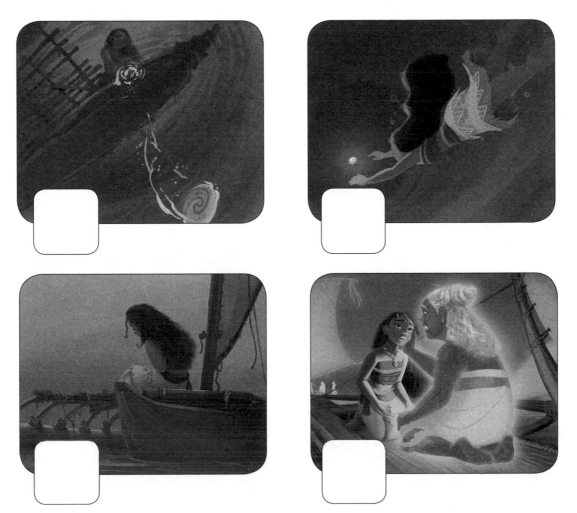

Fill In the Blanks

Chief Bogo gives Judy Hopps 48 hours to find Mr. Otterton. After that, he will fire her.

After is a **sequence word**. It tells you when an event happens.

Fill in the missing sequence word in each sentence. Choose the sequence words from the Word Bank.

Word Bank

After   First   Second   Then

_____, Judy finds Nick Wilde to ask for

his help. _____, they go to a spa and get

some answers from Yax. _____, they look

for the car Yax told them about. _____
they find the car, they ask the car's owner some
questions. He gives them their next clue!

Unscramble the Words

Bellwether is a small sheep. She is tired of being bossed around by predators. She comes up with a plan to get rid of them. She is a clever villain.

Bellwether pretends to be Judy Hopps's friend. Judy is the opposite of a villain. She is a hero!

Unscramble each **purple** word. Fill in the blank.

1. Bellwether is a small **seeph** _____.

2. She plans to get rid of **perdarots** _____.

3. She is a clever **vllaiin** _____.

4. Bellwether pretends to be Judy's **feirdn** _____.

5. Judy is the real **hroe** _____.

67

Matching

Gramma Tala loves teaching Moana about their people.

Match each character to the correct quotation. Write a word to describe the character.

"The ocean chose you," Gramma Tala said, wisely.

_____

"You're welcome!" exclaimed Maui, boldly.

_____

"No one goes past the reef!" Chief Tui said, angrily.

_____

"We can save our island!" Moana shouted, bravely.

_____

Solve the Riddles

There are lots of animals on Moana's island! Heihei is a silly rooster. Pua is a friendly pig. They are Moana's friends.

Read the clues. Solve the riddles. Fill in each blank with the character's name.

1. I have wings.

   I can be silly.

   I make a cock-a-doodle-doo sound.

   Who am I?

   I am _____

2. I am friendly.

   I make an oink sound.

   I like to roll in the mud.

   Who am I?

   I am _____

Picture Search

Judy Hopps and Nick Wilde work together. They solve the mystery of missing mammals in Zootopia!

Identify each story element in *Zootopia*. The **setting** is where a story happens. The **characters** are who the story is about. The **plot** is what happens in the story.

What is the setting of the story?

_____

Who are the main characters?

_____

What is the plot of the story?

_____

_____

HINT Use the picture clues.

Fill In the Blanks

Read the story about a sloth. Label each part of the story. Fill in each box with the correct label.

Word Bank

character   conclusion   plot   setting

1. The jungle is hot and steamy.

2. A sloth hangs from a branch with her long, sharp claws. She slowly reaches for a leaf. The sloth moves so slowly that algae grows on her fur! She blends in with the tree.

3. Suddenly, leaves rustle below. A jaguar slinks among the lower branches.

4. The sloth hangs perfectly still. The jaguar does not notice her. He moves away toward another tree. The sloth is safe!

Out of Order

Gramma Tala is a great storyteller! Telling events in order is part of what makes a great story.

The following events in Moana's story are out of order. Number the events from **1** to **5** to put them in order.

In the end, they make it past Te Kā, return Te Fiti's heart, and save Moana's island.

_____

To save her island, Moana decides to find Maui and return Te Fiti's heart.

_____

Moana's island is in trouble. All the fish are gone and crops are dying.

_____

Their last challenge is getting past Te Kā to reach Te Fiti. They almost give up.

_____

Moana sails past the reef and finds Maui. They face many challenges together!

_____

Solve the Rebus

Mini Maui helps Maui tell stories with pictures.
The story below uses pictures, too.
Fill in each missing word.

Maui brags about what he has done for people.

He says he used his 🪝 _____ to steal

🔥 _____ from the gods. He caught

the sun to make days longer. He caught the

wind so people could ⛵ _____.

He also says he made grass, tides,

🥥 _____, and more.

He really wants to be

admired and take a

🦎 _____.

73

Crossword

Judy uses a picture to find Mr. Otterton. Readers use text features to find information. Answer the clues. Solve the crossword.

Word Bank

CAPTION   DIAGRAM   HEADING   INDEX

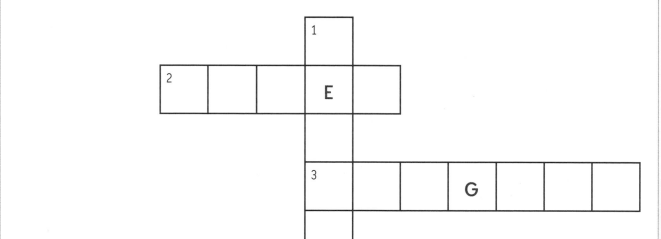

Across

2. list of topics, with page numbers

3. a drawing with labels

4. information about a picture

Down

1. tells you what a chunk of text is about

Fill In the Blanks

Mr. Otterton has turned savage!

Label this diagram of Mr. Otterton for his case file.

Word Bank

eye   ear   mouth   nose   tail

HINT Diagrams give you information.
They can help you understand a topic.

75

Crack the Code

In the beginning, there was only ocean. Then the Mother Island, Te Fiti, appeared. Her heart held the greatest power ever known. It could create life itself! Te Fiti shared her power with the world.

But there were some who wanted the heart for themselves. They thought that if they had it, they could control creation.

The boldest of them all was the trickster demigod, Maui. He could transform himself with his magic fishhook.

Maui used his fishhook to shape-shift into a hawk and steal Te Fiti's heart! As soon as he took the heart, darkness began to spread across the islands.

As Maui flew away with the heart, Te Kā appeared. Te Kā was a demon of earth and fire. She knocked Maui out of the sky. Maui, his hook, and Te Fiti's heart were lost in the ocean.

Darkness has spread ever since. The darkness will end only when Te Fiti's heart is returned to her.

Read each question. (Circle) the letter of the
correct answer.

1. Who is Te Fiti?

   O. the Mother Island   P. the goddess of hearts

2. What is Te Fiti's power?

   B. spreading darkness   C. creating life

3. Who is Maui?

E. a trickster demigod   F. a demon of earth and fire

4. What does Maui steal?

   A. Te Fiti's heart   B. a magic fishhook

5. What will stop the darkness?

   M. Te Kā   N. returning Te Fiti's heart

Fill in the blanks with the letters you circled.
What was there in the beginning?

___ ___ ___ ___ ___

Matching

Judy Hopps asks questions to solve a case.

Reading is like solving a case. You ask yourself questions and think about the answers.

Match **Before reading, During reading,** and **After reading** to the correct question.

Before reading   What did I learn?

During reading   What will this be about?

After reading   What is going to happen next?

Write one question you have about this picture.

_____

_____

Solve the Rebus

Judy Hopps quits the police force and moves back to her parents' farm. What happens next?

Solve the rebus story to find out. Write the missing words beside the images. Then add the missing end punctuation.

Judy hears her dad warn some  _____

not to step on the blue  _____ in the

garden__ Gideon Grey says the flowers are called

night howlers__ "What did you say__" Judy

asks__ Her dad says they keep insects off the

 _____ but make  _____ go

crazy__ Judy gasps__ Night howlers aren't

wolves—they're  _____ __

HINT Statements have **periods**. Questions have **question marks**. Sentences with excitement have **exclamation marks**.

Out of Order

This old subway station is out of order.

So are these sentence parts. Read the parts. Put them in the correct order. Number them **1**, **2**, or **3**.

find an old subway car ____

At the subway station, Nick and Judy ____

filled with night howler plants! ____

To get inside the car, ____

climb through a window. ____

they must sneak past guards and ____

this evidence ____

to the ZPD!" Judy says. ____

"We have to get ____

HINT Look for capital letters and punctuation for clues.

Fill In the Blanks

Judy Hopps and Nick Wilde record Bellwether boasting about her plot. She admits that she's planning to take over Zootopia.

What's next for Bellwether? Fill in the blanks to find out. The missing words are in the Word Bank.

Word Bank

can't   she'll   she's   there's   they've

Judy and Nick tell Bellwether _____ recorded her.

Bellwether knows _____ been caught.

She _____ believe that she was so careless.

She sees that _____ no way to escape.

Now _____ spend years in jail.

HINT Look for clues in the sentence to choose the right contraction.

Matching

Moana lives on an island called Motunui. She found a special stone in the ocean. Moana is a person, Motunui is a place, and a stone is a thing.

Match the nouns below with the labels **person**, **place**, or **thing**.

Chief Tui	place
coconut	person
village	thing
shell	person
island	thing
Gramma Tala	place

HINT A **noun** answers the question who (person), what (thing), or where (place). Think about which question each noun answers.

Colour to Complete

Moana finds something special on the beach. What is it?

To find out, colour the nouns. Use the Colour Key.

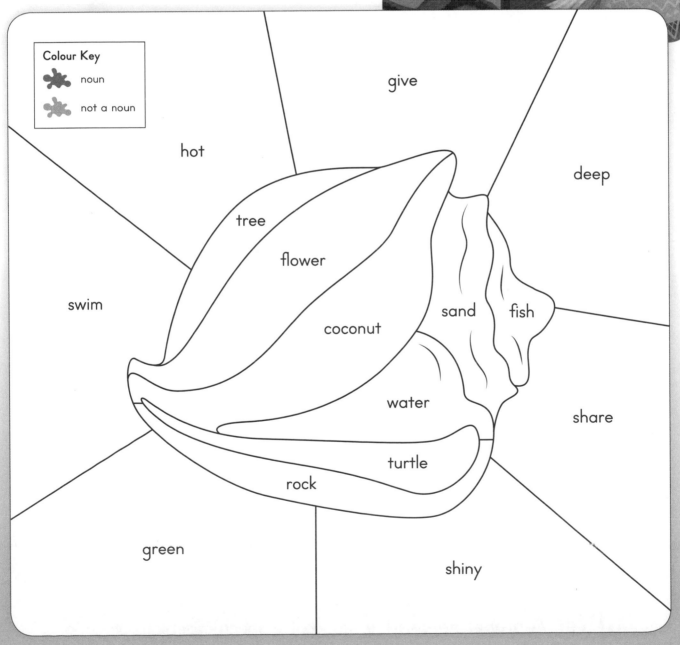

Colour Key

noun

not a noun

give

hot

deep

tree

flower

swim

sand   fish

coconut

water

share

turtle

rock

green

shiny

Maze

Judy Hopps is moving to Zootopia!

Draw a path through the maze.
Follow the proper nouns.

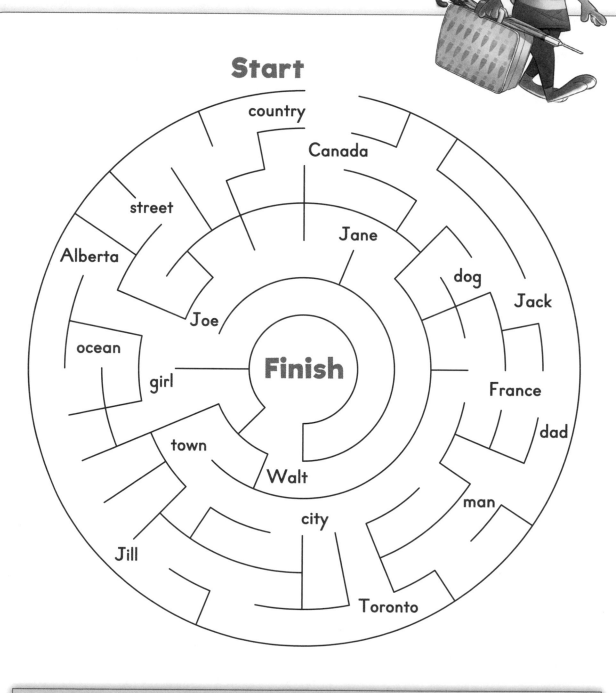

Start

country

Canada

street

Jane

Alberta

dog

Jack

Joe

ocean

girl

Finish

France

dad

town

Walt

man

Jill

city

Toronto

HINT A **proper noun** is the name of a specific person, place, or thing (Judy, Zootopia). Proper nouns start with capital letters.

Word Search

Judy Hopps and Nick Wilde hide under a table to spy on a lab worker.

Hide and **spy** are verbs. **Verbs** are action words.

<u>Underline</u> the verbs in the word list. Next, (circle) the verbs in the word search.

CASE
CATCH
CHASE
CLUE
ESCAPE
FIND
PROVE
SOLVE

B Z R A H R I P R B
C R T O E S O L V E
A O L T X G I N C V
T V B P R O V E S D
C R Y O D L X A T Y
H T P R P V F I N D
M X I N R T O F A L
E S C A P E A Z N D
E T U O V I N T Y K
P E S C H A S E R S

Fill In the Blanks

Something is wrong with Maui's hook!

Something is wrong with the sentences below, too. Some of the verbs are missing! Fill in each blank with the best verb.

Word Bank

are   become   do   does   is

1. Maui and Moana _____ on their way to return Te Fiti's heart.

2. Maui's hook _____ broken.

3. It _____ not work.

4. Maui wants to _____ a hawk but he cannot.

5. What can Maui _____ to fix his hook?

HINT Look for clues in the sentence to choose the best verb.

Crossword

Moana loves to play and swim in the ocean! There are lots of other things to do in and on water. Answer the clues. Solve the crossword!

Word Bank

DIVE   FISH   FLOAT   ROW   VERBS   SKATE

Across

2. What are action words?

5. If you don't sink, you _____.

Down

1. _____ headfirst into water.

3. _____ on frozen water.

4. You do this on a boat; it rhymes with tow.

5. You use a rod and bait to _____.

¹					
²V				³S	
			⁴		
⁵			O	T	
H					

HINT Look at the number of letters for each answer.

Picture Search

The animals in Zootopia feel different emotions. These pictures show some of them.

Look at each picture. (Circle) the adjective that describes how the animals feel.

lonely   loving   angry

bored   cheerful   scared

proud   disappointed   tired

HINT An **adjective** is a word that describes a noun (**smart** bunny).

Colour to Complete

Judy Hopps works hard to earn one of these shiny things. What is it?

To find out, colour the adjectives in the picture. Use the Colour Key.

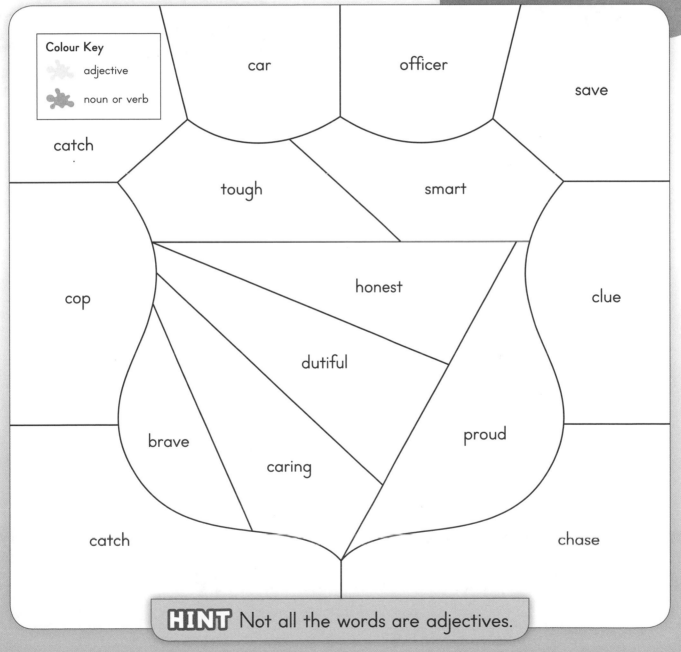

Colour Key

adjective

noun or verb

car

officer

save

catch

tough

smart

cop

honest

clue

dutiful

brave

proud

caring

catch

chase

HINT Not all the words are adjectives.

Fill In the Blanks

Moana learns many things about the past from Gramma Tala.

Complete the sentences below. Fill in the correct verb tense. **Past tense** is for actions that have happened. **Present tense** is for actions happening now.

1. Yesterday, I _____ (**bake / baked**) muffins.

2. I _____ (**walk / walked**) because I want to exercise.

3. They _____ (**add / added**) a flag to the fort they built.

4. Please _____ (**ask / asked**) the question again.

5. I _____ (**pack / packed**) my lunch every day last week.

Crack the Code

Moana overcomes many challenges to return Te Fiti's heart. What is one of her biggest challenges?

To find out, fill in the correct verb tense. Then use the boxed letters to fill in the answer!

I ___ ___ ___ (**eat / ate**) when I am hungry.

I ___ ___ ___ ___ (**feel / felt**) sad when they left.

My team is happy when we ___ ___ ___ (**win / won**).

She ___ ___ ___ ___ (**grow / grew**) taller last year.

I cannot ___ ___ ___ ___ (**leave / left**) before noon.

They ___ ___ ___ ___ (**hold / held**) hands yesterday.

One of Moana's biggest challenges is to

___ b ___ ___ ___ ___ ___ ___ in herself!

Word Search

Judy leaps up and over the police car.

A **preposition** is a word that tells you where something is. **Up** is a preposition. So is **over**.

<u>Underline</u> the prepositions in the word list. Next, (circle) the prepositions in the word search.

BELOW	B E H I N D I P R O
BESIDE	H R T O W T O G D F
INTO	T O L U N D E R C F
NOW	A L B H S E L I P K
OFF	X B E S I D E A T Y
TODAY	I W P E P L D E V W
UNDER	M X I N T O O F A L
BEHIND	P C L U N R I W T R
	E B E L O W N T Y K
	W U N P R E K O W T

Picture Search

Judy Hopps and Nick Wilde go above and beyond to find Mr. Otterton!

Fill in each blank with the correct preposition.

Word Bank

around   between   down   above

The little elephant stands _____ Judy and Nick.

Judy and Nick travel in a gondola

_____ the rainforest.

Judy and Nick get flushed

_____ the toilet.

Judy puts a big doughnut _____ the weasel to catch him.

Fill In the Blanks

A sheep wears a mask and gloves to protect himself. He does not want to touch or breathe in the flowers.

The words **and** and **or** are **conjunctions**, or joining words. So are **but** and **if**. Complete the sentences below. Fill in the blanks with the missing conjunctions.

The flower petals look harmless

_____ they are not.

The sheep will go savage

_____ he touches them.

Word Bank

but   and   or   if

He boils the petals _____ turns them into serum.

Bellwether uses the serum to make predators savage

_____ scare prey.

She must be stopped _____ she'll take control of the city!

HINT Look for clues in the sentence to choose the right conjunction.

Out of Order

Nick Wilde and Judy Hopps are on the job! They work together to keep order in Zootopia.

The sentence parts are out of order. Decide which part comes first and which comes second. Write a **1** or **2** beside each part.

Nick is ready to sign up for the police academy,   _____

but then he hears Judy say that all predators are dangerous.   _____

and makes them into smaller "pawpsicles."   _____

Nick melts down big ice pops   _____

so that she can become the first bunny cop.   _____

Judy works hard   _____

Judy's parents are worried because   _____

they think being a cop is dangerous.   _____

HINT Look for capital letters and punctuation for clues.

Picture Search

This title and picture give you a hint about what to expect in the story. They tell you about the characters, setting, and plot.

Imagine you are writing a story about each picture below. What would the title be? Write it on the lines.

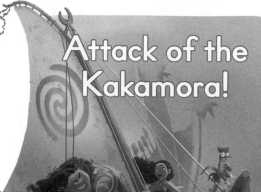

Attack of the Kakamora!

_____

_____

_____

_____

Fill In the Blanks

Moana and her friends have a lot of adventures together!

Complete these sentence starters. Write your own adventure!

Last summer, my family _____

_____ .

We went _____

_____ .

We saw _____

_____ .

We almost _____

_____ .

The best part was _____

_____ !

Silly Sentences

Maui's magic hook turns him into a half-shark. He looks silly! If you had a magic hook, what would you turn into?

Fill in the missing words. Make the sentences as silly as possible!

_____ finds a magic hook! When
　　　your name

_____ picks up the hook, a _____
　　　your name　　　　　　　　　　　　　　　　　　　adjective

thing happens! _____ turns into a
　　　　　　　　　　　　your name

_____ creature.
　　　adjective

One half of the creature is a/an _____.
　　　　　　　　　　　　　　　　　　　　　　　noun

The other half is a/an _____.
　　　　　　　　　　　　　　　　　noun

Now _____ can _____!
　　　　　your name　　　　　　　　　　　　verb

But _____ cannot _____.
　　　　your name　　　　　　　　　　　　verb

HINT A **noun** is a person, place, or thing (**city**). **Adjectives** describe nouns (**big**). **Verbs** are action words (**run**).

Picture Search

After Moana and Maui return Te Fiti's heart, the darkness ends. Moana's people sail again. What adventure do you think Moana will have next?

Look at the picture for ideas. Describe Moana's next adventure.

Answers

Out of Order

Chief Bogo likes to keep order in Zootopia!

There is no order to the letters below. Put them in alphabetical order.

CADB   TRQS
A B C D   Q R S T

ONMP   JKLI
M N O P   I J K L

ZYXW   GEHF
W X Y Z   E F G H

HINT To help you, write the alphabet across the bottom of the page.

4

Word Blocks

Judy Hopps loves everything about being a police officer! She likes law and order.

The **purple** words are out of order. Write them in the word blocks in alphabetical order.

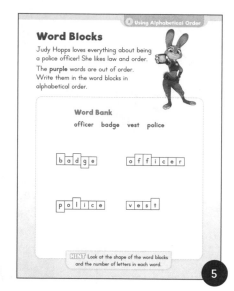

Word Bank

officer   badge   vest   police

b a d g e   o f f i c e r

p o l i c e   v e s t

HINT Look at the shape of the word blocks and the number of letters in each word.

5

Connect the Dots

Moana must go beyond the reef to find Maui! How will she get there? Connect the dots to find out. Follow the words in alphabetical order.

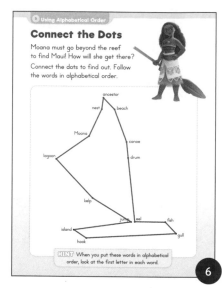

ancestor
nest   beach
Moana   canoe
lagoon   drum
kelp
jump eel   fish
island
hook   gull

HINT When you put these words in alphabetical order, look at the first letter in each word.

6

Puzzle Pieces

When Te Kā is angry, she glows. Red and yellow fire she throws! Match the puzzle pieces to find words that rhyme. Draw a line to connect the pieces with rhyming words.

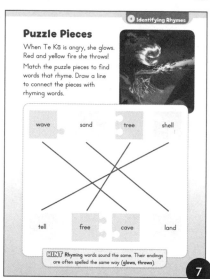

wave   sand   tree   shell

tell   free   cave   land

HINT Rhyming words sound the same. Their endings are often spelled the same way (**glows, throws**).

7

Solve the Rebus

Night howlers are a type of flower. Judy Hopps learns their secret power. **Flower** and **power** rhyme.

Each sentence has a secret word that rhymes with the **purple** word. Fill in each missing word.

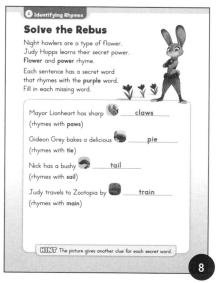

Mayor Lionheart has sharp ___ **claws** ___
(rhymes with **paws**)

Gideon Grey bakes a delicious ___ **pie** ___
(rhymes with **tie**)

Nick has a bushy ___ **tail** ___
(rhymes with **sail**)

Judy travels to Zootopia by ___ **train** ___
(rhymes with **main**)

HINT The picture gives another clue for each secret word.

8

Matching

Many different animals live in Zootopia. Can you name some of them?

Complete the name of each animal. Match each consonant blend with the correct word ending.

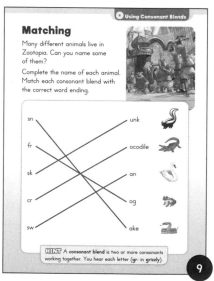

sn   unk
fr   ocodile
sk   an
cr   og
sw   ake

HINT A consonant blend is two or more consonants working together. You hear each letter (**gr-** in **grizzly**).

9

Colour to Complete

Moana has a new friend! Who is hiding under the leaf? Find out by colouring the shapes below. Use the Colour Key.

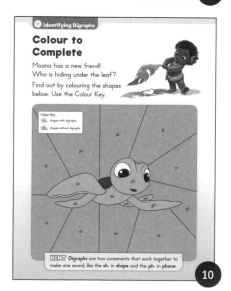

Colour Key
shapes with digraphs
shapes without digraphs

dr   fr
pr
cl   cr
ch   ph
th   wh   gh
sh
tr   sl
st   si
pl

HINT Digraphs are two consonants that work together to make one sound, like the **sh-** in **shape** and the **ph-** in **phone**.

10

Puzzle Pieces

The heart of Te Fiti fits into Te Kā's chest like a puzzle piece! Each consonant blend and digraph below fits with one ending. Draw a line to make a complete word.

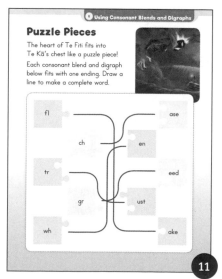

fl   ase
ch   en
tr   eed
gr   ust
wh   ake

11

Fill In the Blanks

Why are so many animals in Zootopia turning savage? To find out, fill in the missing blend or digraph in each **purple** word.

wh   pr   sh   fl   sp

1. Judy Hopps learns that night howlers are _**fl**_owers, not wolves!

2. They can make any animal go crazy, _**pr**_edator or prey!

3. Judy _**sp**_eeds back to Zootopia to find Nick Wilde.

4. They find out _**wh**_o is using night howlers to make animals savage.

5. It is a small _**sh**_eep named Bellwether!

12

---

100   *Sample answers provided.

Word Search

Mr. Big loves his family! The **i** in Big makes a short vowel sound.

In the word list, underline all the words with short vowel sounds. (Circle) the short vowel words in the word search.

ATE	S	R	B	J	Y	S I T		
CAT	Z	U	P	L	Q	I S M		
HOP	Y	N	Z	W	C	C S O		
RUN	H	R	S	N	H	O D M		
SIT	O	B	W E T	D	M	R		
TOE	P	P	P L U	A	P	P		
WET	H	G	Z	P	B	N C S		
	E	M	R	L	C A T E			

HINT Short vowels sound like the vowels in **hat, bet, hit, hot,** and **hut.**

13

Word Blocks

Maui lost his hook! He cannot change shape without it.

The **a** in **change** makes a **long vowel** sound. The **a** in **shape** does, too.

Underline each word in the Word Bank that has a long vowel sound. Write each long vowel word in the correct box.

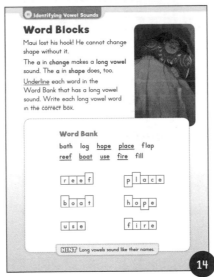

Word Bank

bath   log   hope   place   flap
reef   boat   use   fire   fill

r e e f	p l a c e
b o a t	h o p e
u s e	f i r e

HINT Long vowels sound like their names.

14

Fill In the Blanks

Maui's hook helps him change into different animals.

Sometimes letters change a vowel's sound. Write the missing vowel in each word. Say the word.

f o r k   st a r

c u rl   f u r

p a w   c o w

f i rst   b i rd

HINT Look at the picture to help you figure out the word.

15

Fill In the Blanks

The predators of Zootopia are changing into savage beasts!

Some words change when a silent -e is added to the end. The short vowel becomes a long vowel.

Add a silent -e to each **purple** word. Write the new word on the line. Say each word.

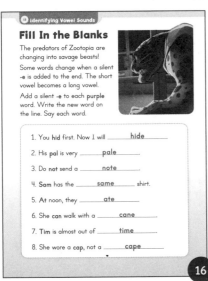

1. You **hid** first. Now I will ___hide___
2. His **pal** is very ___pale___
3. Do **not** send a ___note___
4. **Sam** has the ___same___ shirt.
5. At **noon**, they ___ate___
6. She can walk with a ___cane___
7. **Tim** is almost out of ___time___
8. She wore a **cap**, not a ___cape___

16

Colour to Complete

Officer Clawhauser loves snacks! What is his favourite snack?

To find out, colour the picture. Use the Colour Key.

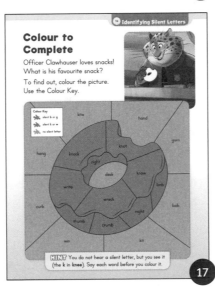

Colour Key
🐾 silent b or g
🐾 silent k or w
🐾 no silent letter

HINT You do not hear a silent letter, but you see it (the **k** in **knee**). Say each word before you colour it.

17

Unscramble the Words

Moana turns her boat away from Te Kā. **Turn** is a verb. A **verb** is an action word.

What are some other verbs for how things move? To find out, unscramble the words.

tworh ___throw___

snip ___spin___

dorp ___drop___

rlol ___roll___

bonuce ___bounce___

trun ___turn___

HINT All the scrambled words are verbs. Each word could complete this sentence: You can _____ the ball.

18

Word Search

Moana finds a hard stone in the clear water. Water is a liquid. A stone is a solid.

Underline words in the list that describe a solid or liquid. (Circle) those words in the word search.

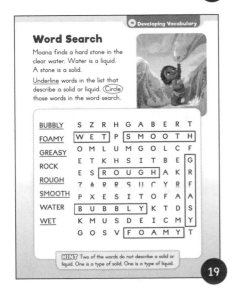

BUBBLY	S	Z	R	H	G	A	B	E	R	T
FOAMY	W E T	P	S M O O T H							
GREASY	O	M	L	U	M	G	O	L	C	F
ROCK	E	T	K	H	S	I	T	B	E	G
ROUGH	E	S	R O U G H	A	K				R	
SMOOTH	Z	A	P	R	S	U	C	Y	R	F
WATER	P	X	E	S	I	T	O	F	A	A
WET	B U B B L Y	K	T	D					S	Y
	K	M	U	S	D	E	I	C	M	Y
	G	O	S	V	F O A M Y	T				

HINT Two of the words do not describe a solid or liquid. One is a type of solid. One is a type of liquid.

19

Maze

A savage jaguar is on the loose! Find an escape through the maze. Follow all the words for mammals.

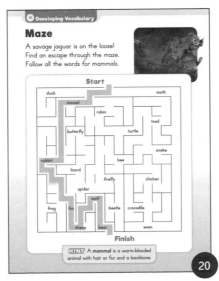

Start

duck   weasel   moth
robin   toad
butterfly   turtle
snake
rabbit   bee
lizard   firefly   chicken
spider
wolf
frog   fox   beetle   crocodile
sheep   bear   swan

Finish

HINT A **mammal** is a warm-blooded animal with hair or fur and a backbone.

20

Matching

Nick melts down frozen jumbo pops. Then he freezes the liquid into many little "pawpsicles." The pops go from solid to liquid to solid.

The pictures show water in different forms. Match each picture to the sentence that describes the water.

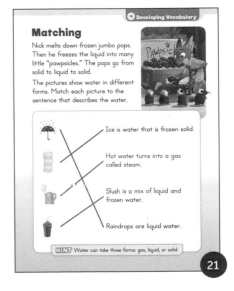

Ice is water that is frozen solid.

Hot water turns into a gas called steam.

Slush is a mix of liquid and frozen water.

Raindrops are liquid water.

HINT Water can take three forms: gas, liquid, or solid.

21

---

*Sample answers provided.

Answers

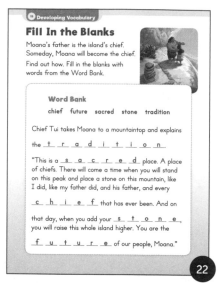

Developing Vocabulary

Fill In the Blanks

Moana's father is the island's chief. Someday, Moana will become the chief. Find out how. Fill in the blanks with words from the Word Bank.

Word Bank

chief   future   sacred   stone   tradition

Chief Tui takes Moana to a mountaintop and explains

the _t_ _r_ _a_ _d_ _i_ _t_ _i_ _o_ _n_

"This is a _s_ _a_ _c_ _r_ _e_ _d_ place. A place of chiefs. There will come a time when you will stand on this peak and place a stone on this mountain, like I did, like my father did, and his father, and every

_c_ _h_ _i_ _e_ _f_ that has ever been. And on

that day, when you add your _s_ _t_ _o_ _n_ _e_, you will raise this whole island higher. You are the

_f_ _u_ _t_ _u_ _r_ _e_ of our people, Moana."

22

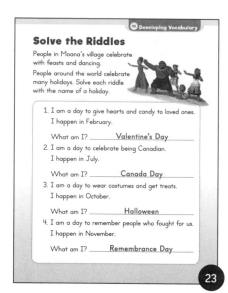

Developing Vocabulary

Solve the Riddles

People in Moana's village celebrate with feasts and dancing.

People around the world celebrate many holidays. Solve each riddle with the name of a holiday.

1. I am a day to give hearts and candy to loved ones. I happen in February.

   What am I? _____Valentine's Day_____

2. I am a day to celebrate being Canadian. I happen in July.

   What am I? _____Canada Day_____

3. I am a day to wear costumes and get treats. I happen in October.

   What am I? _____Halloween_____

4. I am a day to remember people who fought for us. I happen in November.

   What am I? _____Remembrance Day_____

23

Developing Vocabulary

Picture Search

Moana lives on an island. An island is a physical feature.

Look at each picture of a physical feature. Circle the word for it.

(mountain) plain   stream (lake)

lake (river)   (plain) mountain

Developing Vocabulary

Crossword

Moana uses stars to find her way! How else do people find their way? Answer the clues. Solve the crossword.

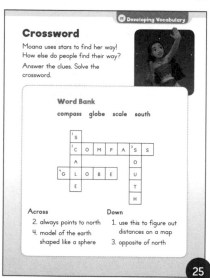

Word Bank

compass   globe   scale   south

```
      ¹S
  ²C O M P A ³S S
      A       O
  ⁴G L O B E   U
      E       T
              H
```

Across
2. always points to north
4. model of the earth shaped like a sphere

Down
1. use this to figure out distances on a map
3. opposite of north

25

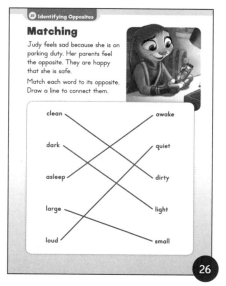

Identifying Opposites

Matching

Judy feels sad because she is on parking duty. Her parents feel the opposite. They are happy that she is safe.

Match each word to its opposite. Draw a line to connect them.

clean   awake

dark   quiet

asleep   dirty

large   light

loud   small

26

Identifying Opposites

Fill In the Blanks

Judy Hopps wants a real case. How can she show Chief Bogo that she is ready?

Fill in the blanks. Write the opposite of the **purple** word that is under the line.

1. The chief thinks Judy

   is too _____small_____
   big

2. He believes she is _____weak_____
   strong

3. How can she be a _____good_____ cop?
   bad

4. She wants to prove him _____wrong_____
   right

5. She will only do her _____best_____!
   worst

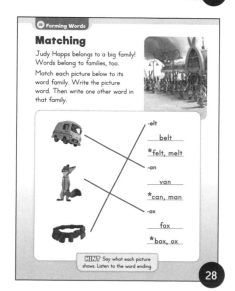

Forming Words

Matching

Judy Hopps belongs to a big family! Words belong to families, too.

Match each picture below to its word family. Write the picture word. Then write one other word in that family.

-elt
   belt
*felt, melt

-an
   van
*can, man

-ox
   fox
*box, ox

HINT Say what each picture shows. Listen to the word ending.

28

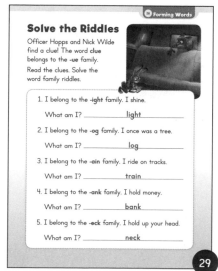

Forming Words

Solve the Riddles

Officer Hopps and Nick Wilde find a clue! The word **clue** belongs to the -ue family.

Read the clues. Solve the word family riddles.

1. I belong to the -ight family. I shine.

   What am I? _____light_____

2. I belong to the -og family. I once was a tree.

   What am I? _____log_____

3. I belong to the -ain family. I ride on tracks.

   What am I? _____train_____

4. I belong to the -ank family. I hold money.

   What am I? _____bank_____

5. I belong to the -eck family. I hold up your head.

   What am I? _____neck_____

29

Forming Plural Words

Picture Search

The Kakamora attack Moana's boat! There are so many of them!

Read the list of objects. Circle at least two of each object in the picture. Write the plural word for each object.

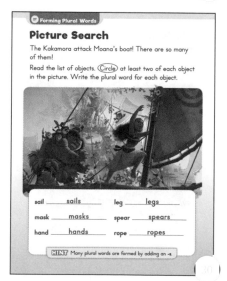

sail _____sails_____   leg _____legs_____

mask _____masks_____   spear _____spears_____

hand _____hands_____   rope _____ropes_____

HINT Many plural words are formed by adding an -s.

---

*Sample answers provided.

Unscramble the Words

Moana loves living on Motunui! What does she love about her island? To find out, unscramble each word.

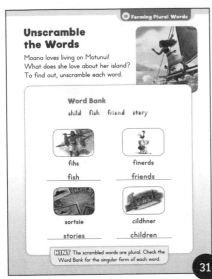

Word Bank

child   fish   friend   story

fihs — **fish**

finerds — **friends**

sortsie — **stories**

cildhner — **children**

> **HINT** The scrambled words are plural. Check the Word Bank for the singular form of each word.

31

Fill In the Blanks

Judy Hopps must finish many tasks to become a police officer! What does Judy have to do? To find out, fill in the missing letters to make the words plural.

Judy must leave her

parent**s**, brother**s**, and sister**s**

to go to the police academy. Her class**es** are

difficult! She must climb wall**s** and swing

across rope course**s**. The other animal**s**

are bigger and stronger. But Judy works hard and

passes all the test**s**. Now she can join

her hero**es** on the police force!

She can battle crook**s** and villain**s**!

> **HINT** Sometimes you need to add -es to make a word plural.

32

Word Search

Judy searches for clues about what happened to Mr. Otterton. The word list has the singular form of each clue. Write the plural form of each clue. Circle the plural form in the word search.

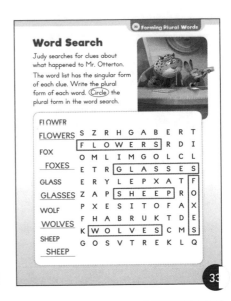

FLOWER
FLOWERS
FOX
FOXES
GLASS
GLASSES
WOLF
WOLVES
SHEEP
SHEEP

```
S Z R H G A B E R T
F L O W E R S R D I
O M L I M G O L C L
E T R G L A S S E S
E R Y L E P X A T F
Z A P S H E E P R O
P X E S I T O F A X
F H A B R U K T D E
K W O L V E S C M S
G O S V T R E K L Q
```

33

Word Blocks

Te Kā hides inside a fiery exterior. Moana can see who Te Kā really is. Can you see the base words hiding inside the **purple words**? Underline each base word. Fill in the word blocks with the base word.

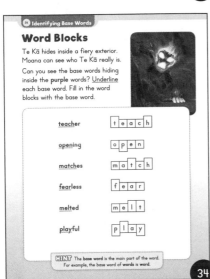

teacher	t e a c h
opening	o p e n
matches	m a t c h
fearless	f e a r
melted	m e l t
playful	p l a y

> **HINT** The base word is the main part of the word. For example, the base word of words is word.

34

Crack the Code

Moana finds a cave filled with huge canoes. Why are they hidden away? To find out, fill in the blanks. Write the base word of each **purple word**. Then use the boxed letters to solve the answer.

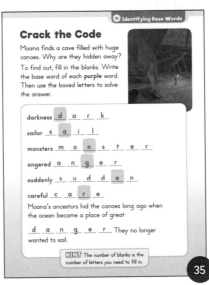

darkness **d a r k**

sailor **s a i l**

monsters **m o n s t e r**

angered **a n g e r**

suddenly **s u d d e n**

careful **c a r e**

Moana's ancestors hid the canoes long ago when the ocean became a place of great

d a n g e r. They no longer wanted to sail.

> **HINT** The number of blanks is the number of letters you need to fill in.

35

Crossword

Moana hears a strange knocking sound inside her canoe! **Knock** is the base word of **knocking**. Each clue has a base word. Underline it. Then write it in the puzzle. Solve the crossword.

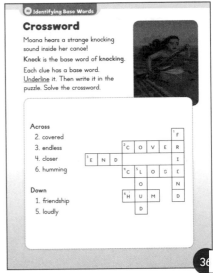

Across
2. covered
3. endless
4. closer
6. humming

Down
1. friendship
5. loudly

```
              ¹F
      ²C O V E R
              R
³E N D         I
      ⁴C L O S E
      O       N
    ⁶H U M     D
      D
```

36

Solve the Riddles

Maui is unhappy. **Unhappy** has the prefix un- and the base word **happy**. Read the clues. Solve the riddles with one of the word choices. Circle the correct word to solve the riddle.

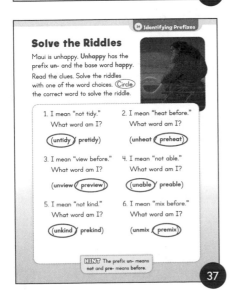

1. I mean "not tidy." What word am I?
(**untidy** / pretidy)

2. I mean "heat before." What word am I?
(unheat / **preheat**)

3. I mean "view before." What word am I?
(unview / **preview**)

4. I mean "not able." What word am I?
(**unable** / preable)

5. I mean "not kind." What word am I?
(**unkind** / prekind)

6. I mean "mix before." What word am I?
(unmix / **premix**)

> **HINT** The prefix un- means not and pre- means before.

37

Matching

Nick Wilde is dishonest when he meets Judy Hopps. She returns him to honesty. The prefix **dis-** means "not." The prefix **re-** means "again." Match the correct prefix with the base word. Draw a line to connect them.

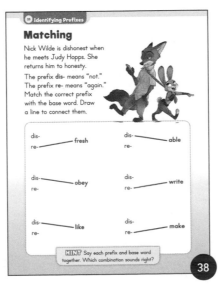

dis-
re- — fresh

dis- — able
re-

dis-
re- — obey

dis-
re- — write

dis-
re- — like

dis- — make
re-

> **HINT** Say each prefix and base word together. Which combination sounds right?

38

Word Search

Judy Hopps and Nick Wilde uncover Bellwether's evil plan! They stop her just in time. In the word list, underline all the words with prefixes. Circle all the words with prefixes in the word search.

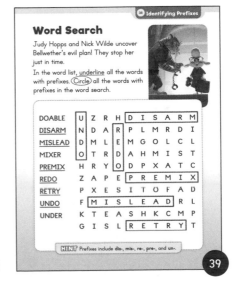

DOABLE
DISARM
MISLEAD
MIXER
PREMIX
REDO
RETRY
UNDO
UNDER

```
U Z R H D I S A R M
N D A R P L M R D I
D M L E M G O L C L
O T R D A H M I S T
H R Y O D P X A T C
Z A P E P R E M I X
P X E S I T O F A D
F M I S L E A D R L
K T E A S H K C M P
G I S L R E T R Y T
```

> **HINT** Prefixes include dis-, mis-, re-, pre-, and un-.

39

Answers

Fill In the Blanks

Officer Judy Hopps is short. She is shorter than Officer Nick Wilde. She is the shortest cop in Zootopia! Adding **-er** and **-est** to words lets you compare things. Complete the sentences below. Add the right suffix to complete each word.

1. A zebra is big. A rhino is bigg___**er**___

   An elephant is the bigg___**est**___ of them all.

2. A butterfly is tiny. A bee is tini___**er**___

   A fly is the tini___**est**___ of them all.

3. Downtown Zootopia is hot. The rainforest

   district is hott___**er**___. Sahara Square is

   the hott___**est**___ of them all.

HINT A suffix attaches to the end of a word. It changes the word's meaning. The suffix **-er** means "more" and **-est** means "most."

40

Fill In the Blanks

The police academy is competitive! How does Judy compare to the other animals there? To find out, fill in the missing **-er** and **-est** suffixes.

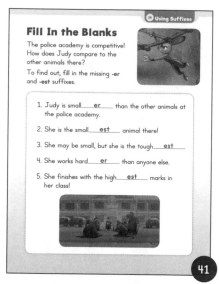

1. Judy is small___**er**___ than the other animals at the police academy.

2. She is the small___**est**___ animal there!

3. She may be small, but she is the tough___**est**___

4. She works hard___**er**___ than anyone else.

5. She finishes with the high___**est**___ marks in her class!

41

Maze

Moana and Maui must escape quickly! **Quickly** has the suffix **-ly**. Draw an escape path through the maze. Follow the words with suffixes.

Start

retake
mislead
hardly
unda
careful
harmless
slowly
Finish
unclear
redo
remake
playful
helpful
mistake
homeless

Puzzle Pieces

Moana and Maui work together against Te Kā. They have great teamwork! **Teamwork** is a compound word. Underline the two words in <u>team</u><u>work</u>. Match the puzzle pieces. Form other compound words.

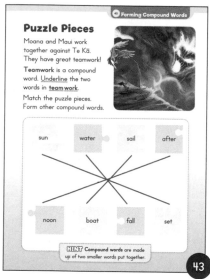

sun   water   sail   after

noon   boat   fall   set

HINT Compound words are made up of two smaller words put together.

43

Solve the Rebus

Moana tricks Tamatoa by replacing the heart of Te Fiti with a plain old rock! Pictures replace the compound word in each sentence. Can you figure out what word the two pictures make? Write the compound word.

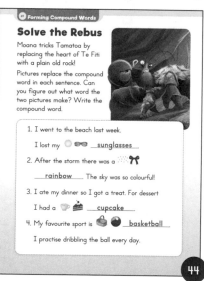

1. I went to the beach last week.

   I lost my ⊙ 👓 ___**sunglasses**___

2. After the storm there was a 🎀

   ___**rainbow**___. The sky was so colourful!

3. I ate my dinner so I got a treat. For dessert

   I had a ☕ 🍰 ___**cupcake**___

4. My favourite sport is 🏀 ___**basketball**___

   I practise dribbling the ball every day.

44

Picture Search

The waves crash against the boat. Some words, like **crash**, sound like what they mean. Think about what is happening in each picture. Circle the word that sounds like what is happening.

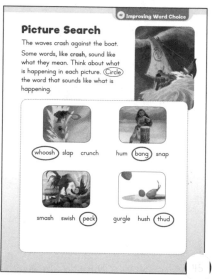

(whoosh)   slap   crunch   hum   (bang)   snap

smash   swish   (peck)   gurgle   hush   (thud)

Fill In the Blanks

Judy Hopps and Nick Wilde shoot out of a pipe. They plunge toward the lake. What is happening to Judy and Nick? The action words **shoot** and **plunge** tell you. The sentences below are missing action words. Choose the best word to complete each sentence.

1. Judy ___**leaps**___ (leaps / crawls / paces) into action when she hears a call for help.

2. Judy ___**races**___ (walks / races / dances) through the streets of Zootopia as fast as she can to catch the thief.

3. The jaguar ___**growls**___ (skips / sings / growls) angrily at Judy and Nick.

4. Everyone ___**cheers**___ (boos / cheers / howls) when Nick becomes a police officer.

HINT Look for clues in the sentence to find the best word.

46

Matching

Judy offers to buy a juicy, fruity jumbo pop for the little elephant. How do you think the jumbo pop tastes? **Fruity** and **juicy** are details about how the jumbo pop tastes. Match each detail below to a sense. Draw a line to connect them.

It is dark inside the asylum. — smell

The wolves' eerie howls echo in the night. — sight

The cold ice wall stings Judy's paws. — taste

Judy takes a bite of the sweet carrot. — sound

Judy breathes the fresh country air. — touch

HINT Details can tell you how something looks, tastes, feels, sounds, or smells.

47

Puzzle Pieces

Officer Hopps must pause when her paws are trapped in wet cement! **Pause** and **paws** are homophones. Match the puzzle pieces to find other homophone pairs. Draw a line to connect the pieces that match.

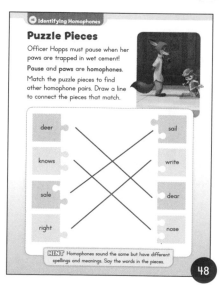

deer   sail

knows   write

sale   dear

right   nose

HINT Homophones sound the same but have different spellings and meanings. Say the words in the pieces.

48

---

*Sample answers provided.

Unscramble the Words

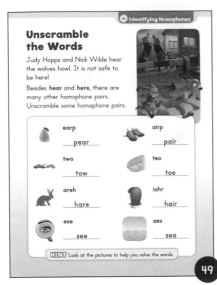

Judy Hopps and Nick Wilde hear the wolves howl. It is not safe to be here!

Besides **hear** and **here**, there are many other homophone pairs. Unscramble some homophone pairs.

earp		airp	
pear		pair	
two		teo	
tow		toe	
areh		iahr	
hare		hair	
ese		aes	
see		sea	

HINT Look at the pictures to help you solve the words.

49

Matching

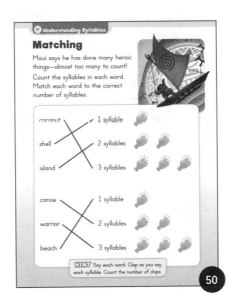

Maui says he has done many heroic things—almost too many to count! Count the syllables in each word. Match each word to the correct number of syllables.

coconut — 1 syllable
shell — 2 syllables
island — 3 syllables

canoe — 1 syllable
warrior — 2 syllables
beach — 3 syllables

HINT Say each word. Clap as you say each syllable. Count the number of claps.

50

Crack the Code

Maui's hook is inside Tamatoa's cave! How do he and Moana get it back? To find out, crack the code. Fill in the blanks from the Word Bank. Then use the letters in the boxes to solve the secret answer!

Word Bank

crab   digs   shiny   skeleton   treasure

t r e a s u r e   (2 syllables)
c r a b   (1 syllable)
d i g s   (1 syllable)
s k e l e t o n   (3 syllables)
s h i n y   (2 syllables)

How do Moana and Maui escape?

Moana t r i c k s Tamatoa!

51

Matching

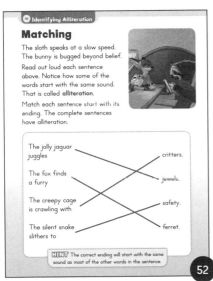

The sloth speaks at a slow speed. The bunny is bugged beyond belief.

Read out loud each sentence above. Notice how some of the words start with the same sound. That is called **alliteration**.

Match each sentence start with its ending. The complete sentences have alliteration.

The jolly jaguar juggles — critters.
The fox finds a furry — jewels.
The creepy cage is crawling with — safety.
The silent snake slithers — ferret.

HINT The correct ending will start with the same sound as most of the other words in the sentence.

52

Unscramble the Words

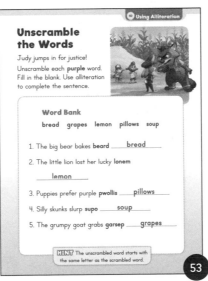

Judy jumps in for justice! Unscramble each **purple** word. Fill in the blank. Use alliteration to complete the sentence.

Word Bank

bread   grapes   lemon   pillows   soup

1. The big bear bakes **beard** bread
2. The little lion lost her lucky **lonem** lemon
3. Puppies prefer purple **pwollis** pillows
4. Silly skunks slurp **supo** soup
5. The grumpy goat grabs **garsep** grapes

HINT The unscrambled word starts with the same letter as the scrambled word.

53

Word Search

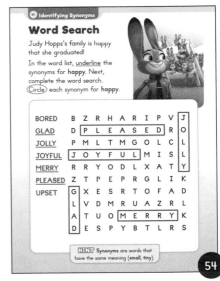

Judy Hopps's family is happy that she graduated!

In the word list, underline the synonyms for **happy**. Next, complete the word search. Circle each synonym for **happy**.

BORED	B Z R H A R I P V J
GLAD	D P L E A S E D R O
JOLLY	P M L T M G O L C L
JOYFUL	J O Y F U L M I S L
MERRY	R R Y O D L X A T Y
PLEASED	Z T P E P R G L I K
UPSET	G X E S R T O F A D
	L V D M R U A Z R L
	A T U O M E R R Y K
	D E S P Y B T L R S

HINT Synonyms are words that have the same meaning (small, tiny).

54

Maze

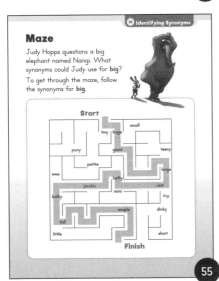

Judy Hopps questions a big elephant named Nangi. What synonyms could Judy use for **big**? To get through the maze, follow the synonyms for **big**.

Start

tiny | huge | small
puny | giant | teeny
petite
wee | large
hefty | vast
bulky | mini | itsy
tall | ample | dinky
little | short

Finish

55

Matching

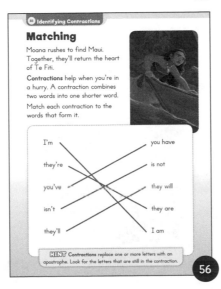

Moana rushes to find Maui. Together, they'll return the heart of Te Fiti.

Contractions help when you're in a hurry. A contraction combines two words into one shorter word. Match each contraction to the words that form it.

I'm — you have
they're — is not
you've — they will
isn't — they are
they'll — I am

HINT Contractions replace one or more letters with an apostrophe. Look for the letters that are still in the contraction.

56

Crack the Code

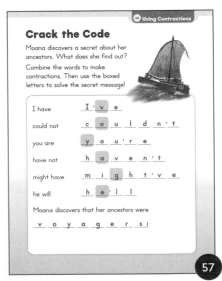

Moana discovers a secret about her ancestors. What does she find out? Combine the words to make contractions. Then use the boxed letters to solve the secret message!

I have   I ' v e
could not   c o u l d n ' t
you are   y o u ' r e
have not   h a v e n ' t
might have   m i g h t ' v e
he will   h e ' l l

Moana discovers that her ancestors were

v o y a g e r s!

57

Answers

Using Picture Clues

Picture Search

Chief Tui is angry. He is frowning. It looks as if he is speaking harshly. What do these pictures tell you about Moana, Gramma Tala, and Maui? (Circle) the best answer to each question.

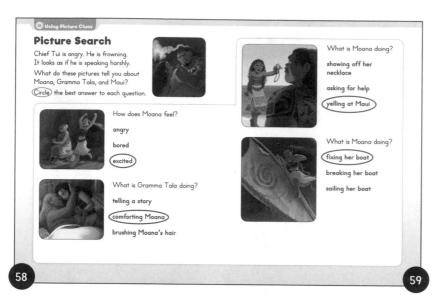

How does Moana feel?
- angry
- bored
- (excited)

What is Gramma Tala doing?
- telling a story
- (comforting Moana)
- brushing Moana's hair

What is Moana doing?
- showing off her necklace
- asking for help
- (yelling at Maui)

What is Moana doing?
- (fixing her boat)
- breaking her boat
- sailing her boat

58   **59**

Making Predictions

Picture Search

Stop, Thief!

Read the title of this story. Look at the picture. What do you think this story is about?

*I think it is about what happens when Judy chases a thief through Rodentia. Judy and the thief are bigger than the cars and buildings. I bet things will get broken.

60

Making Predictions

Picture Search

Judy Hopps and Nick Wilde find out that Mayor Lionheart has all the missing predators locked up! Judy records Mayor Lionheart saying he wants to hide the animals from everyone, including the police! As soon as they can, Judy and Nick tell Chief Bogo what the mayor has been up to.

What do you think happens next? (Circle) that picture.

Explain why you chose that picture.

*The mayor is handcuffed. Chief Bogo is arresting him.

61

Identifying Facts and Opinions

Matching

Read the story. Match each sentence below to the word fact or opinion.

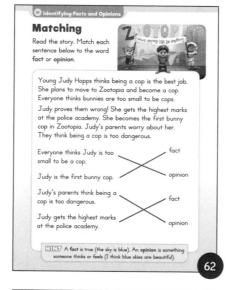

Young Judy Hopps thinks being a cop is the best job. She plans to move to Zootopia and become a cop. Everyone thinks bunnies are too small to be cops. Judy proves them wrong! She gets the highest marks at the police academy. She becomes the first bunny cop in Zootopia. Judy's parents worry about her. They think being a cop is too dangerous.

Everyone thinks Judy is too small to be a cop.   — opinion

Judy is the first bunny cop.   — fact

Judy's parents think being a cop is too dangerous.   — opinion

Judy gets the highest marks at the police academy.   — fact

HINT A fact is true (the sky is blue). An opinion is something someone thinks or feels (I think blue skies are beautiful).

62

Finding Details

Fill In the Blanks

Judy's protective parents hug her tightly. **Protective** is a detail that gives you information.

Fill in the blanks with words from the Word Bank.

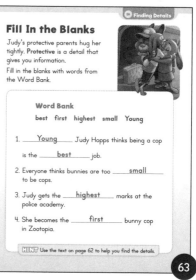

Word Bank
best   first   highest   small   Young

1. _Young_ Judy Hopps thinks being a cop is the _best_ job.

2. Everyone thinks bunnies are too _small_ to be cops.

3. Judy gets the _highest_ marks at the police academy.

4. She becomes the _first_ bunny cop in Zootopia.

HINT Use the text on page 62 to help you find the details.

63

Understanding Story Order

Matching

Stories start with a **beginning**. In the middle is a **problem** and a **solution**. Then comes the **ending**. Match each section of the story to a label.

After many challenges, Moana returns Te Fiti's heart. Moana saves her island!   — beginning

When Moana is sixteen she feels the pull of the ocean. She sails past the reef to find Maui and return the heart.   — problem

Chief Tui does not want his people to sail past the reef. The ocean is too dangerous. Moana is not allowed to return the heart.   — solution

When Moana is a baby, the ocean chooses her to return Te Fiti's heart.   — ending

HINT When you finish, read the sentences in order. The story should make sense from beginning to ending.

64

Understanding Story Order

Out of Order

Read the text. Then look at the pictures. Number the pictures to put them in order.

Moana feels sad. She does not think she can return Te Fiti's heart. She tosses the heart into the ocean. She tells the ocean it made a mistake choosing her. Suddenly, Gramma Tala appears! She shows Moana that she can do it. Moana dives into the water to get the heart. She believes she can finish her task.

2   4   1   3

65

Using Sequence Words

Fill In the Blanks

Chief Bogo gives Judy Hopps 48 hours to find Mr. Otterton. After that, he will fire her.

After is a **sequence word**. It tells you when an event happens.

Fill in the missing sequence word in each sentence. Choose the sequence words from the Word Bank.

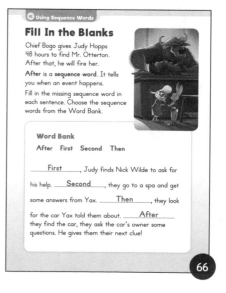

Word Bank
After   First   Second   Then

First, Judy finds Nick Wilde to ask for his help. _Second_, they go to a spa and get some answers from Yax. _Then_, they look for the car Yax told them about. _After_ they find the car, they ask the car's owner some questions. He gives them their next clue!

66

*Sample answers provided.

Unscramble the Words

Bellwether is a small sheep. She is tired of being bossed around by predators. She comes up with a plan to get rid of them. She is a clever villain.

Bellwether pretends to be Judy Hopps's friend. Judy is the opposite of a villain. She is a hero!

Unscramble each **purple** word. Fill in the blank.

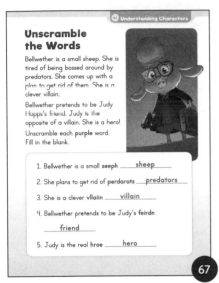

1. Bellwether is a small **seeph** ____sheep____

2. She plans to get rid of **perdarots** ____predators____

3. She is a clever **vllaiin** ____villain____

4. Bellwether pretends to be Judy's **feirdn** ____friend____

5. Judy is the real **hroe** ____hero____

67

Matching

Gramma Tala loves teaching Moana about their people. Match each character to the correct quotation. Write a word to describe the character.

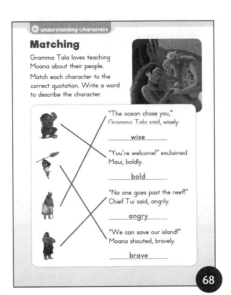

"The ocean chose you," Gramma Tala said, wisely.
____wise____

"You're welcome!" exclaimed Maui, boldly.
____bold____

"No one goes past the reef!" Chief Tui said, angrily.
____angry____

"We can save our island!" Moana shouted, bravely.
____brave____

68

Solve the Riddles

There are lots of animals on Moana's island! Heihei is a silly rooster. Pua is a friendly pig. They are Moana's friends. Read the clues. Solve the riddles. Fill in each blank with the character's name.

1. I have wings.
   I can be silly.
   I make a cock-a-doodle-doo sound.
   Who am I?
   I am ____Heihei____

2. I am friendly.
   I make an oink sound.
   I like to roll in the mud.
   Who am I?
   I am ____Pua____

69

Picture Search

Judy Hopps and Nick Wilde work together. They solve the mystery of missing mammals in Zootopia!

Identify each story element in Zootopia. The **setting** is where a story happens. The **characters** are who the story is about. The **plot** is what happens in the story.

What is the setting of the story?
____Zootopia____

Who are the main characters?
__Judy Hopps and Nick Wilde__

What is the plot of the story?
*Judy and Nick work together to solve the mystery.

HINT Use the picture clues.

70

Fill In the Blanks

Read the story about a sloth. Label each part of the story. Fill in each box with the correct label.

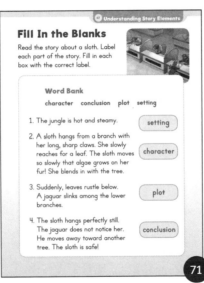

Word Bank

character   conclusion   plot   setting

1. The jungle is hot and steamy. (setting)

2. A sloth hangs from a branch with her long, sharp claws. She slowly reaches for a leaf. The sloth moves so slowly that algae grows on her fur! She blends in with the tree. (character)

3. Suddenly, leaves rustle below. A jaguar slinks among the lower branches. (plot)

4. The sloth hangs perfectly still. The jaguar does not notice her. He moves away toward another tree. The sloth is safe! (conclusion)

71

Out of Order

Gramma Tala is a great storyteller! Telling events in order is part of what makes a great story.

The following events in Moana's story are out of order. Number the events from 1 to 5 to put them in order.

In the end, they make it past Te Kā, return Te Fiti's heart, and save Moana's island. **5**

To save her island, Moana decides to find Maui and return Te Fiti's heart. **2**

Moana's island is in trouble. All the fish are gone and crops are dying. **1**

Their last challenge is getting past Te Kā to reach Te Fiti. They almost give up. **4**

Moana sails past the reef and finds Maui. They face many challenges together! **3**

72

Solve the Rebus

Mini Maui helps Maui tell stories with pictures. The story below uses pictures, too. Fill in each missing word.

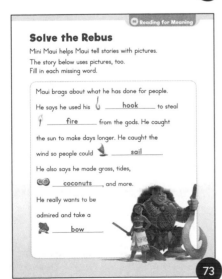

Maui brags about what he has done for people.

He says he used his 🪝 ____hook____ to steal 🔥 ____fire____ from the gods. He caught the sun to make days longer. He caught the wind so people could ⛵ ____sail____

He also says he made grass, tides, 🥥 ____coconuts____, and more.

He really wants to be admired and take a 🐢 ____bow____

73

Crossword

Judy uses a picture to find Mr. Otterton. Readers use text features to find information. Answer the clues. Solve the crossword.

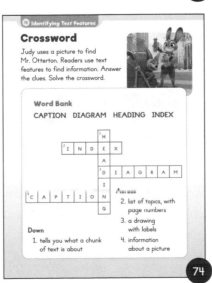

Word Bank

CAPTION   DIAGRAM   HEADING   INDEX

¹H
²INDEX
 A
³DIAGRAM
 I
⁴CAPTION
 N
 G

Across

2. list of topics, with page numbers

3. a drawing with labels

Down

1. tells you what a chunk of text is about

4. information about a picture

74

Fill In the Blanks

Mr. Otterton has turned savage! Label this diagram of Mr. Otterton for his case file.

Word Bank

eye   ear   mouth   nose   tail

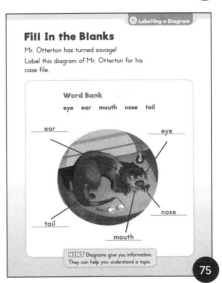

ear

eye

tail

nose

mouth

HINT Diagrams give you information. They can help you understand a topic.

75

*Sample answers provided.

107

Answers

Crack the Code

In the beginning, there was only ocean. Then the Mother Island, Te Fiti, appeared. Her heart held the greatest power ever known. It could create life itself! Te Fiti shared her power with the world.

But there were some who wanted the heart for themselves. They thought that if they had it, they could control creation.

The boldest of them all was the trickster demigod, Maui. He could transform himself with his magic fishhook. Maui used his fishhook to shape-shift into a hawk and steal Te Fiti's heart! As soon as he took the heart, darkness began to spread across the islands.

As Maui flew away with the heart, Te Kā appeared. Te Kā was a demon of earth and fire. She knocked Maui out of the sky. Maui, his hook, and Te Fiti's heart were lost in the ocean.

Darkness has spread ever since. The darkness will end only when Te Fiti's heart is returned to her.

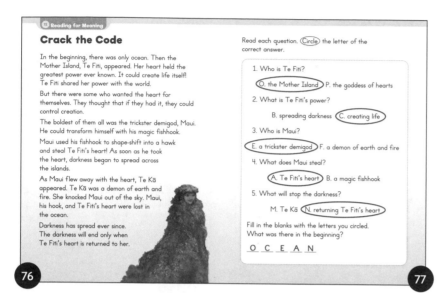

Read each question. (Circle) the letter of the correct answer.

1. Who is Te Fiti?
   (O. the Mother Island) P. the goddess of hearts

2. What is Te Fiti's power?
   B. spreading darkness (C. creating life)

3. Who is Maui?
   (E. a trickster demigod) F. a demon of earth and fire

4. What does Maui steal?
   (A. Te Fiti's heart) B. a magic fishhook

5. What will stop the darkness?
   M. Te Kā (N. returning Te Fiti's heart)

Fill in the blanks with the letters you circled. What was there in the beginning?

<u>O</u> <u>C</u> <u>E</u> <u>A</u> <u>N</u>

76 **77**

Matching

Judy Hopps asks questions to solve a case.

Reading is like solving a case. You ask yourself questions and think about the answers.

Match **Before reading, During reading,** and **After reading** to the correct question.

Before reading — What did I learn?
During reading — What will this be about?
After reading — What is going to happen next?

(lines crossed to match)

Write one question you have about this picture.

____ *Who is Judy talking to?

78

Solve the Rebus

Judy Hopps quits the police force and moves back to her parents' farm. What happens next?

Solve the rebus story to find out. Write the missing words beside the images. Then add the missing end punctuation.

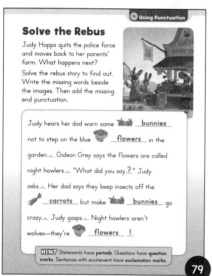

Judy hears her dad warn some 🐰 <u>bunnies</u>

not to step on the blue 🌸 <u>flowers</u> in the

garden<u>.</u> Gideon Grey says the flowers are called

night howlers<u>.</u> "What did you say<u>?</u>" Judy

asks<u>.</u> Her dad says they keep insects off the

🥕 <u>carrots</u> but make 🐰 <u>bunnies</u> go

crazy<u>.</u> Judy gasps<u>.</u> Night howlers aren't

wolves—they're 🌸 <u>flowers</u> <u>!</u>

HINT Statements have **periods**. Questions have **question marks**. Sentences with excitement have **exclamation marks**.

79

Out of Order

This old subway station is out of order.

So are these sentence parts. Read the parts. Put them in the correct order. Number them **1, 2,** or **3**.

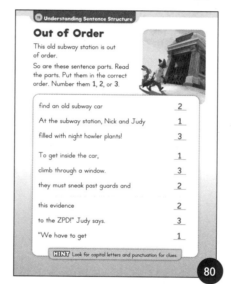

find an old subway car	2
At the subway station, Nick and Judy	1
filled with night howler plants!	3
To get inside the car,	1
climb through a window.	3
they must sneak past guards and	2
this evidence	2
to the ZPD!" Judy says.	3
"We have to get	1

HINT Look for capital letters and punctuation for clues.

80

Fill In the Blanks

Judy Hopps and Nick Wilde record Bellwether boasting about her plot. She admits that she's planning to take over Zootopia. What's next for Bellwether? Fill in the blanks to find out. The missing words are in the Word Bank.

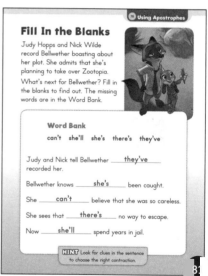

Word Bank
can't she'll she's there's they've

Judy and Nick tell Bellwether <u>they've</u> recorded her.

Bellwether knows <u>she's</u> been caught.

She <u>can't</u> believe that she was so careless.

She sees that <u>there's</u> no way to escape.

Now <u>she'll</u> spend years in jail.

HINT Look for clues in the sentence to choose the right contraction.

81

Matching

Moana lives on an island called Motunui. She found a special stone in the ocean. Moana is a person, Motunui is a place, and a stone is a thing.

Match the nouns below with the labels **person, place,** or **thing.**

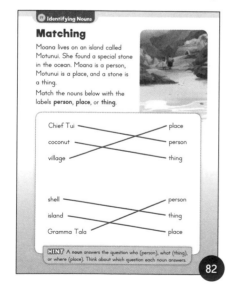

Chief Tui — place
coconut — person
village — thing
(lines crossed to match)

shell — person
island — thing
Gramma Tala — place
(lines crossed to match)

HINT A **noun** answers the question who (person), what (thing), or where (place). Think about which question each noun answers.

82

Colour to Complete

Moana finds something special on the beach. What is it?
To find out, colour the nouns. Use the Colour Key.

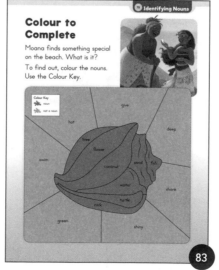

Colour Key
🌸 noun
🐚 not a noun

83

Maze

Judy Hopps is moving to Zootopia! Draw a path through the maze. Follow the proper nouns.

Start ... Finish

HINT A **proper noun** is the name of a specific person, place, or thing (Judy, Zootopia). Proper nouns start with capital letters.

84

108

*Sample answers provided.

Word Search

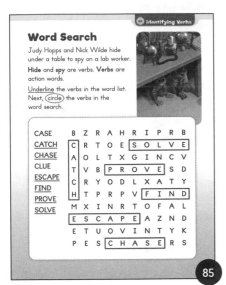

Judy Hopps and Nick Wilde hide under a table to spy on a lab worker.

Hide and **spy** are verbs. **Verbs** are action words.

<u>Underline</u> the verbs in the word list. Next, (circle) the verbs in the word search.

CASE	B Z R A H R I P R B
<u>CATCH</u>	C R T O E [S O L V E]
<u>CHASE</u>	A O L T X G I N C V
CLUE	T V B [P R O V E] S D
<u>ESCAPE</u>	C R Y O D L X A T Y
<u>FIND</u>	H T P R P V [F I N D]
<u>PROVE</u>	M X I N R T O F A L
<u>SOLVE</u>	[E S C A P E] A Z N D
	E T U O V I N T Y K
	P E S [C H A S E R] S

Fill In the Blanks

Something is wrong with Maui's hook! Something is wrong with the sentences below, too. Some of the verbs are missing! Fill in each blank with the best verb.

Word Bank
are   become   do   does   is

1. Maui and Moana ___are___ on their way to return Te Fiti's heart.

2. Maui's hook ___is___ broken.

3. It ___does___ not work.

4. Maui wants to ___become___ a hawk but he cannot.

5. What can Maui ___do___ to fix his hook?

HINT Look for clues in the sentence to choose the best verb.

Crossword

Moana loves to play and swim in the ocean! There are lots of other things to do in and on water. Answer the clues. Solve the crossword!

Word Bank
DIVE   FISH   FLOAT   ROW   VERBS   SKATE

Across

2. What are action words?

5. If you don't sink, you _____.

Down

1. _____ headfirst into water.

3. _____ on frozen water.

4. You do this on a boat; it rhymes with tow.

5. You use a rod and bait to _____.

HINT Look at the number of letters for each answer.

Picture Search

The animals in Zootopia feel different emotions. These pictures show some of them.

Look at each picture. (Circle) the adjective that describes how the animals feel.

lonely   (loving)   angry

bored   cheerful   (scared)

(proud)   disappointed   tired

HINT An **adjective** is a word that describes a noun (**smart** bunny).

Colour to Complete

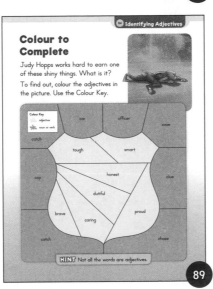

Judy Hopps works hard to earn one of these shiny things. What is it?

To find out, colour the adjectives in the picture. Use the Colour Key.

Colour Key
adjective
noun or verb

car   officer   solve
catch
tough   smart
honest
cop   clue
dutiful
brave   proud
caring
catch   chase

HINT Not all the words are adjectives.

Fill In the Blanks

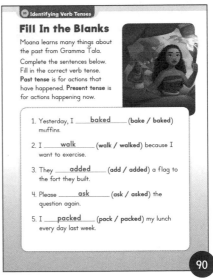

Moana learns many things about the past from Gramma Tala.

Complete the sentences below. Fill in the correct verb tense. **Past tense** is for actions that have happened. **Present tense** is for actions happening now.

1. Yesterday, I ___baked___ (bake / baked) muffins.

2. I ___walk___ (walk / walked) because I want to exercise.

3. They ___added___ (add / added) a flag to the fort they built.

4. Please ___ask___ (ask / asked) the question again.

5. I ___packed___ (pack / packed) my lunch every day last week.

Word Search

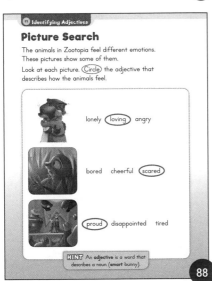

Judy leaps up and over the police car.

A **preposition** is a word that tells you where something is. **Up** is a preposition. So is **over**.

<u>Underline</u> the prepositions in the word list. Next, (circle) the prepositions in the word search.

<u>BELOW</u>	[B E H I N D] I P R [O
<u>BESIDE</u>	H R T O W T O G D F
<u>INTO</u>	T O L [U N D E R] C F]
NOW	A L B H S E L I P K
<u>OFF</u>	X [B E S I D E] A T Y
TODAY	I W P E P L D E V W
<u>UNDER</u>	M X [I N T O] O F A L
<u>BEHIND</u>	P C L U N R I W T R
	E [B E L O W] N T Y K
	W U N P R E K O W T

Word Search

Judy leaps up and over the police car.

A **preposition** is a word that tells you where something is. **Up** is a preposition. So is **over**.

<u>Underline</u> the prepositions in the word list. Next, (circle) the prepositions in the word search.

<u>BELOW</u>	[B E H I N D] I P R [O
<u>BESIDE</u>	H R T O W T O G D F
<u>INTO</u>	T O L [U N D E R] C F]
NOW	A L B H S E L I P K
<u>OFF</u>	X [B E S I D E] A T Y
TODAY	I W P E P L D E V W
<u>UNDER</u>	M X [I N T O] O F A L
<u>BEHIND</u>	P C L U N R I W T R
	E [B E L O W] N T Y K
	W U N P R E K O W T

Picture Search

Judy Hopps and Nick Wilde go above and beyond to find Mr. Otterton!

Fill in each blank with the correct preposition.

Word Bank
around   between   down   above

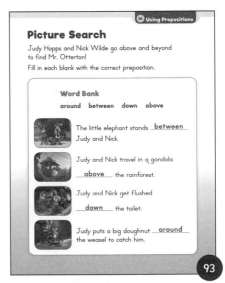

The little elephant stands ___between___ Judy and Nick.

Judy and Nick travel in a gondola ___above___ the rainforest.

Judy and Nick get flushed ___down___ the toilet.

Judy puts a big doughnut ___around___ the weasel to catch him.

---

*Sample answers provided.

109

Answers

Fill In the Blanks

A sheep wears a mask and gloves to protect himself. He does not want to touch or breathe in the flowers.

The words and and or are conjunctions, or joining words. So are but and if. Complete the sentences below. Fill in the blanks with the missing conjunctions.

The flower petals look harmless __but__ they are not.

Word Bank

but   and   or   if

The sheep will go savage __if__ he touches them.

He boils the petals __and__ turns them into serum.

Bellwether uses the serum to make predators savage __and__ scare prey.

She must be stopped __or__ she'll take control of the city!

HINT Look for clues in the sentence to choose the right conjunction.

94

Out of Order

Nick Wilde and Judy Hopps are on the job! They work together to keep order in Zootopia.

The sentence parts are out of order. Decide which part comes first and which comes second. Write a 1 or 2 beside each part.

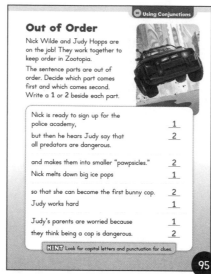

Nick is ready to sign up for the police academy, __1__

but then he hears Judy say that all predators are dangerous. __2__

and makes them into smaller "pawpsicles." __2__
Nick melts down big ice pops __1__

so that she can become the first bunny cop. __2__
Judy works hard __1__

Judy's parents are worried because __1__
they think being a cop is dangerous. __2__

HINT Look for capital letters and punctuation for clues.

95

Picture Search

This title and picture give you a hint about what to expect in the story. They tell you about the characters, setting, and plot.

Imagine you are writing a story about each picture below. What would the title be? Write it on the lines.

Attack of the Kakamora!

*Moana's Adventures Past the Reef

*Escape from the World of Monsters!

96

Fill In the Blanks

Moana and her friends have a lot of adventures together! Complete these sentence starters. Write your own adventure!

Last summer, my family *went on a camping trip

We went *to a forest with a lake

We saw *birds, squirrels, and raccoons.

We almost *got lost on a hike one day

The best part was *having a campfire every night !

97

Silly Sentences

Maui's magic hook turns him into a half-shark. He looks silly! If you had a magic hook, what would you turn into? Fill in the missing words. Make the sentences as silly as possible!

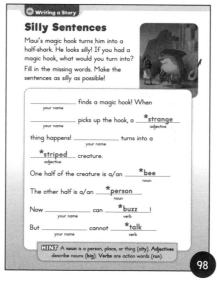

_____ finds a magic hook! When
your name

_____ picks up the hook, a *strange
your name   adjective

thing happens! _____ turns into a
               your name

*striped creature.
adjective

One half of the creature is a/an *bee
                                  noun

The other half is a/an *person
                        noun

Now _____ can *buzz !
    your name   verb

But _____ cannot *talk
    your name   verb

HINT A noun is a person, place, or thing (city). Adjectives describe nouns (big). Verbs are action words (run).

98

Picture Search

After Moana and Maui return Te Fiti's heart, the darkness ends. Moana's people sail again. What adventure do you think Moana will have next?

Look at the picture for ideas. Describe Moana's next adventure.

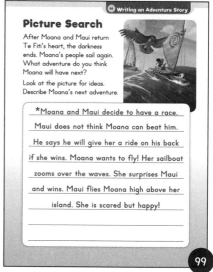

*Moana and Maui decide to have a race. Maui does not think Moana can beat him. He says he will give her a ride on his back if she wins. Moana wants to fly! Her sailboat zooms over the waves. She surprises Maui and wins. Maui flies Moana high above her island. She is scared but happy!

99

---

*Sample answers provided.

Cut out these flash cards. Use them to practise reading and forming words.

ack

ook

een

ing

ill

oke

ock

ore

ump

Answers

been, green, keen, preen, queen, screen, seen, teen

Answers

book, brook, cook, crook, hook, look, nook, took

Answers

back, black, crack, flack, hack, lack, pack, rack, sack, shack, slack, snack, stack, tack, track, whack

Answers

awoke, bloke, broke, choke, joke, poke, smoke, spoke, stoke, woke, yoke

Answers

bill, chill, dill, drill, fill, frill, gill, grill, hill, ill, kill, mill, pill, quill, sill, skill, spill, still, till, will

Answers

bring, cling, fling, king, ping, ring, sing, sling, spring, sting, string, swing, thing, wing, wring, zing

Answers

bump, clump, dump, grump, hump, jump, lump, plump, pump, rump, slump, stump, thump, trump

Answers

bore, chore, core, fore, gore, lore, more, ore, pore, score, shore, sore, spore, store, swore, tore, wore, yore

Answers

block, clock, crock, dock, flock, frock, hock, jock, knock, lock, mock, rock, shock, smock, sock, stock

Cut out these flash cards. Use them to practise reading and forming words.

Cut out these flash cards. Use them to practise reading and forming words.

wh___

th___

pre___

ch___

ph___

dis___

sp___

un___

re___

Answers

space, spade, speak, spell, spider, spin, spoon, sports, spot

Answers

chain, chair, chase, cheer, chest, chin, choose, chop

Answers

whale, what, wheel, when, where, while, whip, who, whole

Answers

unable, unclean, undo, uneven, unlucky, unreal, unripe, unsafe, untidy, unwanted, unwell

Answers

phase, photo, phone, phony

Answers

than, that, the, then, these, thick, this, thorn, those, three, throw

Answers

reappear, redo, remix, remove, rename, replay, rerun, retell, review

Answers

disable, disagree, disappear, dishonest, dislike, disobey

Answers

prefix, preheat, preload, premade, prepay, preview

Cut out these flash cards. Use them to practise reading and forming words.

Cut out these flash cards. Use them to practise reading and forming words.

_ly

_less

_ful

solid

liquid

gas

ocean

mountain

plain

Answers

careful, fearful, graceful, hopeful, hurtful, painful, skillful, thankful, useful, wishful

Answers

endless, fearless, hopeless, painless, restless, spotless, thankless, useless

Answers

bravely, clearly, darkly, deeply, loudly, quickly, quietly, safely, softly, slowly, tightly

scale

compass

mammals

holiday

celebration

tradition

Cut out these flash cards. Use them to practise reading and forming words.

Congratulations

_____!

Print your name.

You have finished the
Brain Boost learning path.
Way to go!